King Kamehameha IV and Queen Emma
Founders of The Queen's Hospital

The Queen's Medical Center
Commemorating 150 years
Of providing health care to the people of Hawai'i

THE
QUEEN'S
MEDICAL CENTER

HALE MAʻI O KA WAHINE ALIʻI

*Published on the occasion of
the one hundred and fiftieth anniversary
of its founding*

JASON Y. KIMURA

HONOLULU

page i
Native Hawaiian women on the palm-lined drive leading to the entrance of The Queen's Hospital, circa 1880s.

pages ii–iii
The Queen Emma Building lobby, circa 1925. Completed in 1924, the building was later renamed the Nalani Wing, and still stands today.

page iv
The Queen's Conference Center. Originally called the Mabel Leilani Smyth Memorial Building, this historic structure was designed by C. W. Dickey and completed in 1941.

pages vi–vii
Doctors, nurses, and patients in the Queen Emma Building, circa 1924. For more than a hundred years since the hospital's founding in 1859, the buildings of Queen's were open air. Even as late as the 1970s, many patient areas were still not air-conditioned. The striped awnings that once graced the windows of Queen's façade were a familiar sight during the mid-twentieth century. Wood-backed wheelchairs, like the ones shown in the photograph, were used until recently; the last two were finally retired in 2009.

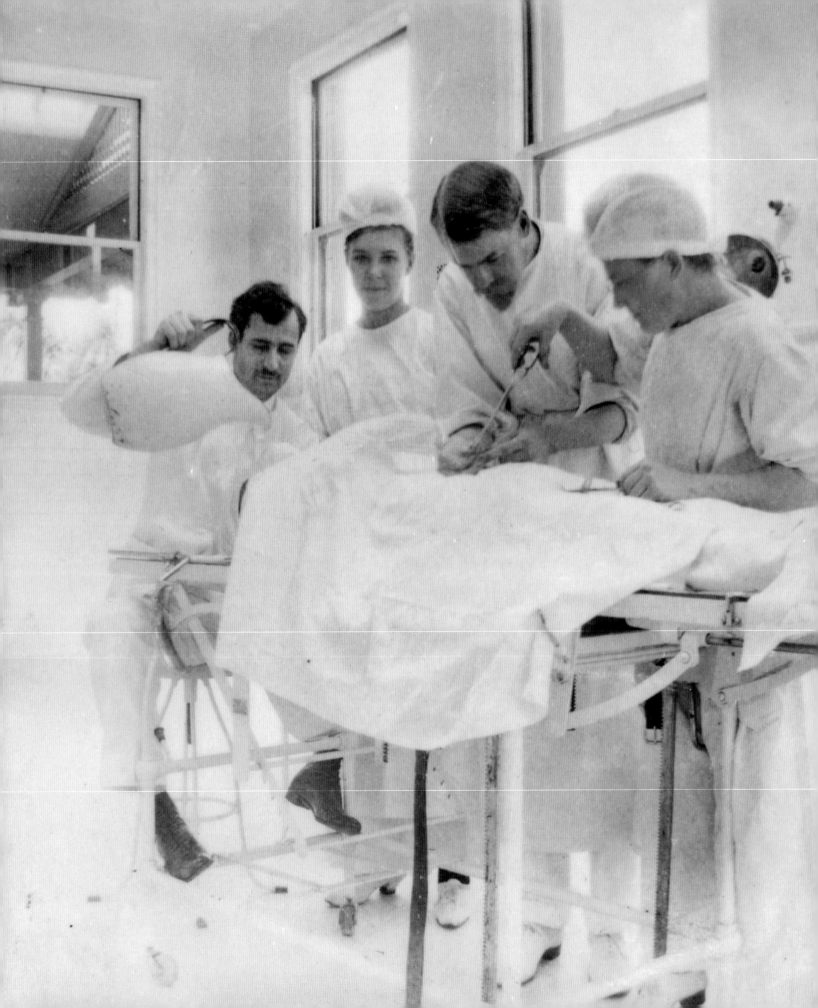

CONTENTS

A successful surgery in the Pauahi Wing's third floor operating room, 1908. Dr. H. R. Hunt (second from right) is aided by an unknown assistant. Miss Starret, operating nurse, looks at the camera, while Dr. L. L. Sexton administers anesthesia with an enameled pitcher.

DEDICATED TO

Margery Hastert

1911-2004

Queen's beloved volunteer historian, who became the curator of the Queen's Historical Room in 1965 when it was established, and who tirelessly collected and preserved the history of Queen's for thirty-nine years.

The first students of The Queen's Hospital Training School for Nurses, Christmas 1916. Of thirty-one students, only ten graduated after the three-year program was completed in 1919.

overleaf
The grounds of The Queen's Medical Center, 2009.

A View of Diamond Head from Queen Street. 1856. In the background is Kawaiaha'o Church. Built in 1841, the historic church looks almost the same today as it did in the nineteenth century, although the bell tower was then a pointed spire. In 1860, the king, accompanied by a procession, marched from the Stone Church, as it was sometimes called, up Punchbowl Street for the laying of the cornerstone of The Queen's Hospital.

A block beyond the church are the Mission Houses, built in the 1820s. There wasn't much beyond these houses in the 1850s: Thatched grass dwellings dotted the landscape, and there was a clear view all the way to Diamond Head, which the Hawaiians called Leahi. In the foreground on the right are the walls of Hono- lulu Fort, from which Fort Street derives its name. The two-story building just beyond it is the courthouse, which was where the early trustees of The Queen's Hospital held their meetings.

PROLOGUE

A fitting place to begin to discover the history of The Queen's Hospital is the memorial for Native Hawaiians who died during the smallpox epidemic of 1853–54. Numerous introduced diseases decimated the Hawaiian population, but the smallpox epidemic was the catalyst that led King Kamehameha IV and Queen Emma to establish Queen's in 1859. A mere 150 years is a short span of time, but the vast differences in how the people of Hawai'i lived in the nineteenth century and the way we live today makes our understanding opaque, lost in dull and dusty tomes and obscured by modern redevelopment. What was Honolulu like in 1859 and the years after the establishment of The Queen's Hospital (now known as The Queen's Medical Center)? Can we go back in time and regain a sense of what it was like to walk through the wards at the original Queen's building? How did Queen's evolve into the modern medical center it is today?

The memorial is a short walk from The Queen's Medical Center. Proceeding from Queen's toward the waterfront on Punchbowl Street, remnants of nineteenth-century Honolulu can be seen on every street. Crossing Punchbowl near Miller Street is a manhole cover dated 1899, the year Honolulu's sewer system was installed. When the Punchbowl site was purchased in 1860, it was a dry, desolate place. The streets, which were unpaved dirt roads, were rarely just right. A pedestrian would likely have been walking along a hot, dusty Punchbowl Road, or one sodden with mud. To the right, near the intersection of Punchbowl and Beretania streets, is Washington Place, built in 1846 by New England sea captain John Dominis. His son, Governor John Owen Dominis, lived there after his father's death in 1847 and christened it "Washington Place," after George Washington. In 1862, Dominis married Lydia K. P. Kapa'akea, who would become Queen Lili'uokalani after her husband's death. Ahead is the 'Iolani Palace. During the days of King Kamehameha IV and Queen Emma, there was an older, simpler 'Iolani Palace, which looked more like a mansion with a large veranda encircling it. It was torn down to clear the way for the current palace, completed in 1882.

Farther down Punchbowl is Kawaiaha'o Church, where Alexander Liholiho ascended the throne to become King Kamehameha IV in 1854, and where he gave his maiden speech to the legislature. This was also where he would marry Emma Rooke, who became Queen Emma.

Looking toward Honolulu Harbor from this vantage point, one would have been able to see the masts of whaling and merchant ships docked at the piers. Continuing down Punchbowl and rounding the corner of the Kawaiaha'o Church graveyard at Queen Street, one comes face to face with the old redbrick brewery. Its engraved stone sign says, "The Honolulu Brew'g & Malt'g C, 1900." The smallpox memorial is located behind this building, but the only way to get to it is via Quinn Lane, a lonely, dead-end street.

The memorial, planted with ti leaf and well kept, is the remnant of a cemetery that once stretched all the way to the Kaka'ako Fire Station, more than a block east. A bronze plaque reads: "E Moe Me Ka Maluhia [rest in peace]. This sacred site, a remnant of the Honuakaha Cemetery, is set aside in perpetuity to honor Native Hawaiian victims of the smallpox epidemic that occurred between 1853 and 1854, many of whom rest peacefully herein." The epidemic broke out in May 1853 and lingered in the rural areas of O'ahu until January 1854. There were at least 6,400 cases of smallpox and about 2,500 deaths, virtually all among the native population. The actual numbers were probably much higher. In any case, the Native Hawaiian population was reduced to 71,019 after the epidemic.

It wasn't the first devastating epidemic, and it wouldn't be the last.

A Woman of Honolulu. 1852.
Scandinavian artist Carl J. A. Skogman noted that Hawaiian women typically wore wide dresses
that tied around the neck, had long and loose sleeves, and hung freely to the ankles.

HALE MAʻI O KA WAHINE ALIʻI

Hospital of the Chiefess

During the smallpox epidemic of 1853, teams of horse-drawn, covered yellow wagons, heavily laden with the dead, could be seen every day on the streets of Honolulu, traveling from one ravaged house to another. Because there were so many deaths in the later stages of the epidemic, graves at the Honuakaha Cemetery were dug only wide enough to bury bodies lying on their sides. Between the arrival of Captain Cook in 1778 and the first official census in 1853, introduced diseases—syphilis, gonorrhea, bubonic plague, cholera, typhoid, influenza, measles, dysentery, tuberculosis, and smallpox—as well as war and famine, had reduced Hawaiʻi's population by more than 75 percent, from some 300,000 to 71,000. Many earlier epidemics had taken more lives, but the 1853 epidemic, both rapid and deadly, came at a time when the population was already decimated. This defining trial would lead a kingdom's new, young leaders, Kamehameha IV and Queen Emma, to the founding of The Queen's Hospital.

The Scars of an Epidemic

On February 10, 1853, the American merchant ship *Charles Mallory* arrived at Honolulu Harbor flying a yellow flag, which signaled a contagiously sick passenger or crewmember. The ship had come from the West Coast of the mainland, where smallpox was rampant. The person with smallpox was isolated, and everyone else on board was quarantined and vaccinated. In this instance, no new cases appeared. Honolulu resumed its normal routine, and the minister of public instruction oversaw a general vaccination campaign.

On May 13, a man reported to the office of William Cooper Parke, marshal of the Hawaiian Islands, that two Hawaiian women who lived on Maunakea Street in downtown Honolulu were sick, and that he suspected smallpox. A guard was placed at the house, allowing no one to leave or enter. In his *Personal Reminiscences*, Parke recalls that by May 16, the legislature passed an act to allow King Kamehameha III to appoint three commissioners of health to take charge of containing the disease. The commissioners were Dr. Gerritt Parmele Judd, Dr. Thomas Charles Byde Rooke, and Parke.

Although some think the May outbreak stemmed from the *Charles Mallory*, the new cases most likely came from another source, given the amount of time that had elapsed since the ship was in port. Parke later reported that a week before arriving in Honolulu, the captain of a merchant ship had slept in a room in San Francisco next to someone who had died of smallpox. The partitions between the sleeping quarters were made of brown cotton cloth, and the captain had hung his clothing against them. When he arrived in Honolulu, he gave his clothes to the two women to wash.

The women were moved to a building on Queen Street hastily set up as a hospital, and their house was burned to the ground. It was too late. The commissioners appointed subcommissioners on the other islands, and immediately mandated measures to prevent the spread of smallpox and stamp it out wherever it was found. The commission would eventually involve Prince Alexander Liholiho, the future King Kamehameha IV; the experience would give the nineteen-year-old prince firsthand experience with the plight of his people.

Thomas G. Thrum, publisher of the *Hawaiian Annual*, recalled his arrival in Hawaiʻi on May 16, 1853, as a ten-year-old boy:

Shortly after arrival I was made aware of the first smallpox infected premises, on Maunakea street, by its yellow flags and being roped off across the street.... I do not recall that any other premises were so quarantined, though it was not

NOTE: Many of the sources referenced for this book are unpublished documents that belong to the Queen's Historical Room and the Hawaiʻi Medical Library.

long before the disease was prevalent in all parts of the town, so that the health authorities and the doctors were taxed to the utmost to combat it. Our house … was soon in the midst of infection, and the piteous, dismal wail of bereaved ones in the neighborhood, day after day, told the sad story of its steady progress.[1]

By the middle of June, forty-one people had died and 114 were sick. The next week, the numbers doubled. During the height of the epidemic, it was not uncommon to find only dead bodies at a dwelling place, and fifty bodies were being buried every day. Knowledge of smallpox was limited at the time, and there was disagreement among doctors on how to deal with the epidemic. Thrum continues:

The town crier (kuahaua) … [was] the one to announce official proclamations during the smallpox period … a little old man with good lung power. His cries were not confined to street corners, but at intervals along the way he would shout his "E Hoolohe" (O Listen), then pour forth his announcement as he trudged along.[2]

 The frequency of the "dead cart" on the streets to receive bodies, many of them simply wrapped in mats, called for heroic work by a force of employees of the health authorities to prevent secret interments on the premises. A prominent fearless worker at this duty was a prisoner named John Robinson,

known as "three-fingered Jack," for which valiant service he was given his liberty and a goodly sum of money at the close of the siege.[3] … Toward the end of July some forty houses at Waikiki and thirty on the Ewa side of Honolulu, two miles from town center, were being erected for the reception of patients.[4]

Although physicians rushed to vaccinate as many people as they could, virtually all smallpox cases occurred in the Hawaiian population. Parke recalls only one foreigner dying from the disease—the man in charge of the hospital on Queen Street. He stated that "there had been but little general vaccination among the natives, so the disease had a clear field." Vaccination against smallpox had been practiced in Hawai'i since 1839, but natives were slow to adopt Western medicine. Many refused to be vaccinated and actively avoided it. Furthermore, they were panic stricken and horrified by the overwhelmed "pest houses," where the sick were taken to languish. The healthy fled the city, and facing separation from their families, the sick did so as well, and the disease spread across O'ahu.

 Prince Alexander Liholiho replaced Dr. Judd as one of the commissioners when the latter was ousted. Parke explains:

During the prevalence of the disease … considerable excitement was caused by some persons who made a political affair of it, charging Dr. Judd and Mr. Armstrong as the persons who

were responsible for the introduction of the disease. A more willful accusation could not be imagined; but certain ones who had ill-feelings against the former carried the matter so far that he [Judd] was removed from office.[5]

The Report of the Royal Health Commissioners to the king was signed T.C.B. Rooke, W. C. Parke, and Liholiho. The commissioners reported 6,405 cases of smallpox and 2,485 deaths—a death rate of almost 39 percent.[6]

A New Hope for Health

William Cooper Parke wrote: "Kamehameha III had been seriously sick for about a week, when he died at the Palace on Friday, the 15th of December, 1854, at a quarter to twelve A.M." Emotions were torn in opposite directions as shouts of joy could be heard from the people for the popular young Liholiho, while natives numbering two thousand from all over town gathered on the lawn of 'Iolani Palace to grieve for "Kamehameha the good."[7]

On January 11, 1855, less than a month before his twenty-first birthday, Alexander Liholiho was administered the oath of office at Kawaiaha'o Church. At the opening of the legislature in 1855, he addressed many issues, but saved his most urgent directive for last:

opposite   Honolulu and Nu'uanu Valley, circa 1853.
above   *Upper Fort Street.* 1867. The area above Beretania Street was a quiet, residential area with white picket fences and feathery algeroba trees (also known as keawe or mesquite). Mauna Ala, the Royal Mausoleum, which was completed in 1864, appears in the background in Nu'uanu Valley.

The Smallpox Hospital in Waikīkī. Circa 1853. The Swiss artist Paul Emmert was among the *Charles Mallory* passengers quarantined in this hospital, which was located in an uninhabited area on the edge of what is now Kapi'olani Park. The yellow flag indicates the presence of smallpox.

The Trustees of The Queen's Hospital

The king served as President of the Board of Trustees during the days of the monarchy. The trustees have served without compensation from the founding of The Queen's Hospital to the present. The number of trustees (called directors during the mid-twentieth century and now called trustees again) has changed several times over the years. When Queen's became a private, nonprofit entity in 1909, the number of trustees was reduced from twenty to seven.[8] Currently, there are fourteen trustees.[9] Many of the names of Queen's trustees from the nineteenth century are still familiar today or represent the men who shaped the very essence of Hawai'i in its formative years.

The homes of Charles Reed Bishop, Captain Luce, and the Reverend Samuel C. Damon, 1850s.

A subject of deeper importance . . . than any I have hitherto mentioned, is that of the decrease of our population. It is a subject, in comparison with which all others sink into insignificance. . . . Our acts are in vain unless we can stay the wasting hand that is destroying our people. I feel a heavy, and special responsibility resting upon me; . . . we [shall not] be acquitted by man, or our Maker, of a neglect of duty, if we fail to act speedily and effectually in the cause of those who are every day dying before our eyes. . . . I would commend to your special consideration the subject of establishing public Hospitals.[10]

In response, the legislature passed a law authorizing the minister of the interior to set up two hospitals "for the sick poor, being natives of this kingdom." Although $5,000 was appropriated, the government's weak financial position prevented action. At the opening of the legislature in 1856, the king again addressed the need for hospitals, but the financial position of the government was not improved. Bills for the establishment of hospitals were passed in subsequent years through 1859, but did not provide revenue.

Establishing The Queen's Hospital

The Queen's Hospital was not the first hospital in Hawai'i. However, most early institutions provided only the most basic care. The earliest catered mainly to seamen of various countries. The American Hospital, established in 1837 in Waikīkī, offered better care than most others, which operated in the back rooms of liquor saloons—called grog shops—and were little more than places to sleep off a night's revelry. For example, the Hospital for English Seamen, opened in 1841, was located in a drafty, thatched hut next to a grog shop.[11] Hawai'i's first true private hospital was the "Hydrop establishment" in Nu'uanu Valley, founded in 1852. It didn't survive very long; the following year, it was replaced by Dr. Ford's City Hospital "for the treatment of invalids, residents or strangers."[12] It became clear that none of these were adequate.

King Kamehameha IV married Emma Nā'ea Rooke on June 19, 1856, and the new queen gave birth to a son, Albert, on May 20, 1858. Queen Emma, who was the adopted daughter of Dr. T.C.B. Rooke, immediately took interest in the proposed hospital. Through her urging, a joint committee was assembled to set up a dispensary and lay the general groundwork for a hospital project. At the specific urging of the queen, the king signed an act for the organization and incorporation of an association for the establishment of a hospital "for the relief of sick and destitute Hawaiians" on April 20, 1859. The corporation would also be able to "provide for sick and disabled seamen of other countries, or patients of any description who are fit subjects for hospital treatment." A passenger's tax and a seamen's tax on seamen sailing under the Hawaiian flag would be levied to help finance the hospital. When the corporation had raised $5,000, the minister of the interior, Prince Lot Kamehameha (later Kamehameha V), could give the corporation an equal amount in government lands or the money from the sale thereof.[13]

Queen Emma had the idea of collecting subscriptions for the hospital. An attempt was made to form a committee of ladies for this purpose, and a day was suggested for commencing the work, but "obstacle after obstacle intervened, and at last her majesty, disappointed at not being able to carry out a favored plan, requested that the King himself would undertake the labor of love which she had hoped to execute in person."[14] It is not known whether the king originally envisioned being a literal foot soldier for the cause, but according to the Cabinet Council Minute Book, as early as 1857 he did entertain the idea of seeking voluntary contributions to fund a hospital, perhaps influenced by Queen Emma.

It was whaling season when the king began his solicitations. The docks of Honolulu Harbor were forested with the masts of the ships, interconnected by their weblike rigging, and the putrid odor of their dead prey wafted in with the trade winds. The town enjoyed the business of two to three thousand crewmen, and the ships' captains were generally in a cheerful mood after a long, brutal arctic season. The king could often be seen where they congregated, trying to interest the captains in the charitable work of a new hospital. Shunning the mark of his position as much as possible, he often wore white linen and donned a fine Panama hat.[15] Accompanied by his secretary, who carried a memorandum book to record pledges, or subscriptions, as they were called, the king also called on diplomats, businesses, and private citizens, whether the day was clear or the streets muddy from rain. He went up and down Fort Street and "the byways of Honolulu."

When the king and his cabinet met on May 24, they decided to name the new hospital The Queen's Hospital,

in recognition of Queen Emma's passion and vision in its establishment. At a public meeting of the subscribers held at the courthouse the next day, the king announced that subscriptions from some 250 businesses, groups, and individuals had totaled $13,530, of which $695 had already been paid. Two levels of subscribers were established. Subscribers who contributed $10 or more, but less than $50, for two consecutive years would be considered annual members, and those who gave $50 or more would be life members.[16] The king and the queen headed the list of subscribers with pledges of $500 each (about $13,356.27 in 2008 dollars).[17] (Although all countries' coins were given legal tender status, U.S. currency was the standard since Hawai'i's economy was closely tied to the United States.)[18]

Eight resolutions were adopted. In part, it was resolved that the corporation be called The Queen's Hospital Corporation and that the king and queen be considered Royal Patrons of the hospital. It was also resolved that the board of trustees would comprise a president and twenty subscribers—ten subscribers were to be elected at the meeting, and ten would be nominated by the minister of the interior to represent the government. The trustees were charged with applying for a Charter of Incorporation and were given the power to "establish all by-laws, direction, and control of the institution." They were further authorized to "establish a temporary dispensary with suitable hospital accommodations,"[19] and to find a permanent site as quickly as possible.[20]

Chosen by ballot to be trustees on behalf of the subscribers were B. F. Snow, S. C. Damon, J. N. Castle, C. R. Bishop, J. W. Austin, E. O. Hall, J. T. Waterhouse, W. A. Aldrich, W. L. Green, and H. Hackfeld. Appointed to represent the government were HRH Prince Kamehameha, W. C. Parke, G. M. Robertson, T. C. Heuck, John Ladd, James Bissett, H.J.H. Holdsworth, A. B. Bates, and John Montgomery, with one temporary vacancy due to death. The list boasted prominent members of the community who had exceptional ability. Although some of the government appointees were controversial, and the king lost his temper and gave sharp rebukes, the meeting ended in a general spirit of satisfaction. The king was named President of the Board of Trustees by enthusiastic acclamation.[21]

Meanwhile, fundraising continued. On May 26, 1859, the king and queen attended a benefit concert by the Musical

HALE MA'I O KA WAHINE ALI'I

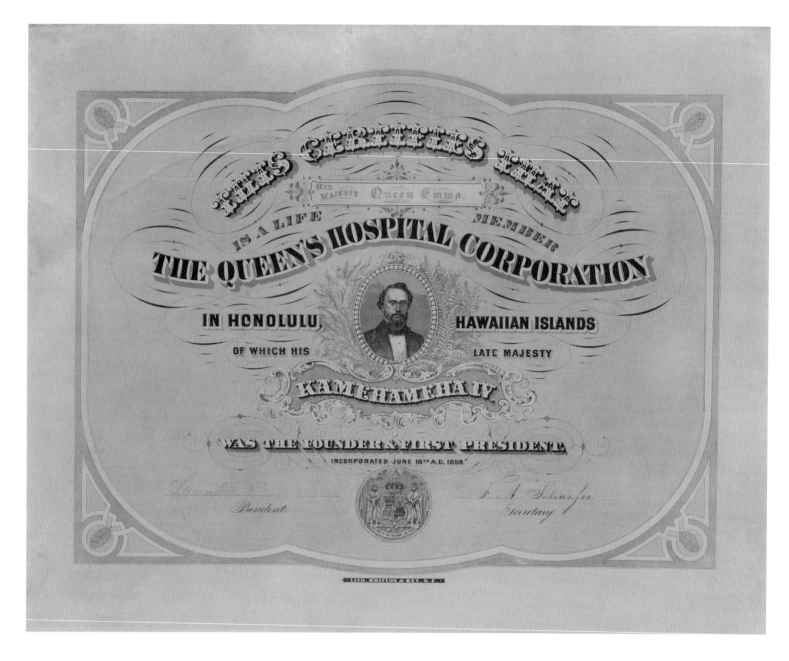

The Queen's Hospital Corporation certificate of life membership for Her Majesty Queen Emma.

THIS CERTIFIES THAT HER MAJESTY Queen Emma IS A LIFE MEMBER OF THE QUEEN'S HOSPITAL CORPORATION IN HONOLULU, HAWAIIAN ISLANDS OF WHICH HIS LATE MAJESTY KAMEHAMEHA IV WAS THE FOUNDER & FIRST PRESIDENT. INCORPORATED JUNE 16TH A.D. 1859.

President   Secretary

Queen Emma's certificate of life membership in The Queen's Hospital Corporation. Though undated, the lithograph is signed by William Lunalilo, who reigned only during the year of 1873 before succumbing to tuberculosis.

opposite
The home of Dr. William Hillebrand, 1850s.

Amateur Society. Held at the Fort Street Church, the event was well attended "by all who had a dollar to spare," according to *The Polynesian*. The concert netted $218.75.[22] Another fundraiser on November 9 of that year was a magic show that garnered $309.25.[23]

The Queen's Hospital Corporation's charter was signed on June 20, 1859. The purpose of the hospital was "for the relief of indigent sick and disabled people of the Hawaiian Kingdom, as well as of such foreigners and others as may desire to avail themselves of the same."[24] The trustees were also to receive sick and invalid seamen of other nations and patients of any description who were fit subjects for medical or surgical treatment. Although the charter does not specifically mention free treatment for Hawaiians, as a government-supported entity, the hospital provided free treatment to anyone who couldn't pay, provided that they were properly admitted and that sufficient funds were available. The trustees reinforced the definition of "the people of the Hawaiian Kingdom" in 1863 by resolving that "all indigent sick and disabled Hawaiian subjects, native and naturalized, are entitled to receive accommodation and treatment at The Queen's Hospital, and that the number of patients of that class can alone be limited by the pecuniary [ability] of the corporation to provide for them."[25] It was also understood that those who could afford to pay would be charged. The Hawaiian-language newspaper, *Nupepa Kuokoa*, was scathing in its comments regarding a person who took advantage of the hospital's free treatment when he could have paid: "A man who goes to this hospital when he could afford to pay is like a thief who steals taro from the mouths of the poor."

William (Wilhelm) Hillebrand (1821–1886)

There was considerable interest in becoming the physician of The Queen's Hospital among doctors in Honolulu. To ensure they would be able to offer the best medical care available, the trustees offered a salary of $1,500 a month ($40,068 in 2008 dollars).[26] Dr. William Hillebrand was selected by majority vote of the trustees.

Hillebrand was born on November 13, 1821 in Nieheim, Westphalia, a province of Prussia. After completing his early education in Nieheim, Hillebrand studied in Göttingen, Heidelberg, and Berlin. After earning his medical degree in Berlin, he began a practice in Paderborn, Germany. However, an illness, thought to be pulmonary tuberculosis, forced Dr. Hillebrand to find a better climate. He sailed to Australia and the Philippines and began to practice medicine in Manila, but poor health caused him to move on. He traveled to San Francisco, and then arrived in Hawai'i on December 28, 1850. His health improved considerably, so Hillebrand decided to stay, and in the fall of 1852 he opened a practice with Dr. Wesley Newcomb. That year, he married Newcomb's stepdaughter, Miss Anna Post, with whom he had two sons.

Hillebrand soon established a successful practice with Hawaiian royalty as patients. He served as the physician of

The Queen's Hospital until he left the islands in 1871. In addition to his work at Queen's, Hillebrand became a member of the Board of Health in 1863 and was a physician at the O'ahu Insane Asylum for a while, beginning in 1868. He owned a drug store with Dr. J. Mott-Smith at Hotel and Fort streets, and was one of the signers of the Charter of Incorporation of the Hawaiian Medical Society. Hillebrand was a "quiet, sober, practical man of medium height and weight, complexion fair, eyes gray and as possessing an abundance of rather dark hair. He was fond of his family and took a particular interest in the education of his children, two sons, William Francis and Henry Thomas. . . . The doctor was very fond of music . . . but his favorite recreation was that of working among his horticultural specimens at his home garden."[27]

In 1865, before leaving with his family on a yearlong world tour via the Orient, Hillebrand was commissioned by various boards and societies to perform numerous tasks during his trip. The Privy Council appointed him Commissioner of Immigration and directed him to look for workers from the Orient to replace native workers, whose numbers were rapidly dwindling. Hillebrand arranged for Chinese and Japanese contract laborers in 1865 and 1868, respectively, and later recruited a pioneer group of 180 Portuguese from Madeira and the Azores, who arrived in Hawai'i in 1878. At the request of the Board of Health, Hillebrand investigated methods of controlling leprosy. One of his foremost tasks during the tour was to collect plants and animals considered valuable additions to the Hawaiian Islands. The Royal Hawaiian Agricultural Society, with which Hillebrand was associated, financed the purchases. According to the *Hawaiian Gazette*

HALE MA'I O KA WAHINE ALI'I

of July 28, 1866, the doctor forwarded ten Wardian cases (forerunner of the terrarium) from Singapore, nine from Calcutta, one from Ceylon, eight from Java, and two from China. The collection of plants included camphor, jak fruit, litchi, mandarin orange, Chinese plum, Java plum, several types of eugenias and banyans, and a considerable number of other useful and ornamental plants. Hillebrand also imported numerous species of birds, including Japanese finches, Chinese quail, Indian sparrows, and mynah birds.[28] The doctor planted many rare and exotic trees and plants at Queen's, as well as at his home on Nuʻuanu Avenue, which later became the Foster Botanical Gardens.

Dr. Hillebrand and his family left Hawaiʻi on June 27, 1871. He spent some time in Cambridge, Massachusetts, where he began the manuscript for his *Flora of the Hawaiian Islands*, which cataloged 250 species of rare plants then unknown to the botanical world. After traveling extensively in Europe, the doctor settled in Heidelberg. Although very ill for the two years before his death in 1886, Hillebrand managed to complete his book; his son, Dr. William Francis Hillebrand, a chemist, helped edit the book, and it was published posthumously in 1888.

The Queen's Dispensary

In the middle of July 1859, a building for the dispensary was rented for $60 a month from Thomas Thrum, the father of the future publisher of the *Hawaiian Annual*, quoted previously. Located at the foot of Fort Street at the intersection of King Street, the dispensary was large and airy. The main business thoroughfares at the time were King and Nuʻuanu streets; Fort Street was rather quiet. However, downtown Honolulu near the Queen's dispensary was as colorful as it is today. Hawaiian burden-bearers trudged along the streets trying to find buyers for their calabashes of poi, vegetables, fowl, or pig, which were balanced on either end of an *aumaka* (pole). Milk vendors set up during the morning hours on certain street corners, called "milk stand." "Poi market" was where sellers arranged their calabashes along the curb of the sidewalk. Vendors promoting their product directly or by colorful *oli* (chants) would have twenty or more open calabashes of poi ready for passersby to dip their fingers into and test one batch after another.[29]

Opened to the public on August 1, 1859, the Thrum

building was outfitted as a dispensary for outpatients with eighteen beds for "boarding inmates." The Thrum building would be the home of The Queen's Hospital until March 1860. On August 3, *Ka Hae Hawaiʻi* announced (translated from Hawaiian):

The new hospital is opened on King Street, by Pukolo. The doctor, Kaukamakaʻāinana [literally, "the people's doctor," presumably Hillebrand], is ready to care for the sick, and to administer medicine to the indigent sick at no cost, if they previously obtain documentation from one of the caregivers of the said Queen's Hospital. Therefore, O ailing people, go there and receive the medicine to cure you promptly; don't lie in your house and die. Go from 7:30 until 9 in the morning, daily; and on Sunday, between the hours of 8 and 9.

The *Pacific Commercial Advertiser* added, "The native name fixed on as synonymous with The Queen's Hospital and by which it will be known among natives is ʻHale mai o Ka Wahine Alii [Hospital of the Chiefess].'"[30]

In closing that year's session of the legislature, the king expressed great satisfaction in the establishment of The Queen's Hospital:

You, Representatives, . . . have expressed a kind and grateful feeling for the personal share which I and the Queen have taken in the labor of securing the necessary means for the establishment of a Hospital in Honolulu. Whilst acknowledging your courtesy I wish to take this first public occasion to express the almost unspeakable satisfaction with which I have found my efforts successful beyond my hopes. It is due to the subscribers as a body, that I should bear witness to the readiness . . . with which they have met my advances. . . . Let the fact be made known, that in Honolulu the sick man has a friend in everybody. Nor do I believe that He who made us all . . . has seen with indifference how the claims of common humanity have drawn together, in the subscription list, names representative of almost every race of men under the sun.[31]

As the only physician, the duties of Dr. Hillebrand at the temporary dispensary were to "fit up one room as a surgery and dispensary,"[32] and select and arrange a proper supply of medicines. He was to be at the dispensary for at least an hour and a half a day, but not more than three (later, at least three hours), and was to prescribe appropriate medicines and examine every patient who requested admission. Hillebrand was required to report on all cases at the next executive committee meeting and admit those patients who were given an admission certificate by the executive committee chairman. Responsible for the supervision of the hospital and its staff, he was charged with establishing hospital rules and with keeping records of all cases. He was provided with an assistant, known as the purveyor, whose duties were to help manage the hospital by keeping track of finances and business contracts, to procure the necessary supplies, and to hire other staff. An assistant physician was not added until 1869, and there were no nurses until 1886. Instead, family members, relatives, or friends, called *kokua* (helper) or *makamaka* (close friend), cared for the patient.

The executive committee of the board of trustees exercised considerable control over patient admissions. The trustees were given blank certificates of admission that read: "I recommend (blank) living at (blank) and suffering from (blank) as a proper person to receive gratuitous hospital relief, being unable to pay for advice and medicines. (signed by trustee)." Even paying patients had to have executive committee consent. Emergency patients were admitted without consent, but the committee would later decide whether hospital care should be continued. These procedures seem to have been instituted to keep track of hospital funds.[33]

Over a hundred patients were treated during the first month, of whom just three paid for treatment. There were ten "boarding inmates," as inpatients were called. In just over two months, twenty-five people were accepted as inmates, and fifteen of these were released, with twelve pronounced cured. During that first month, 965 medical consultations took place, and some of the destitute outpatients received free meals. The total cost of caring for patients and feeding the staff for the month was $97 (about $2,600 in 2008 dollars).[34] Although most of the patients were Hawaiian, many natives stayed away out of fear, preferring the familiarity of their *kahuna la'au lapa'au* (Hawaiian herbal medicine healers).

For the first five months, Dr. Hillebrand reported a total of 765 applicants, or eighteen to twenty per day on average. On stormy days, the number declined to fewer than ten, while good weather brought in as many as thirty-five. Fifty-four people were accepted as patients of the hospital during

Man of the Hawaiian Islands. 1852. A burden-bearer carries an *aumaka* (pole), on which he balances calabashes holding poi, vegetables, fowl, or pork for sale.

this initial period; forty-three of those left the hospital, four died (tuberculosis, typhoid fever, croup, and pulmonary apoplexy), and seven were still at the hospital. Of the forty-three patients who departed, thirty-nine were pronounced cured, two were incurable, and two ran away.[35] In addition, Hillebrand gave five to six consultations per day, and 2,160 prescriptions were dispensed.

During this first five-month period, the trustees were busy with financial issues. Special attention had to be given to unpaid subscriptions, which totaled $4,850. The trustees approved hiring a collector, and a year later, with $1,400 still unpaid, the *Pacific Commercial Advertiser* threatened

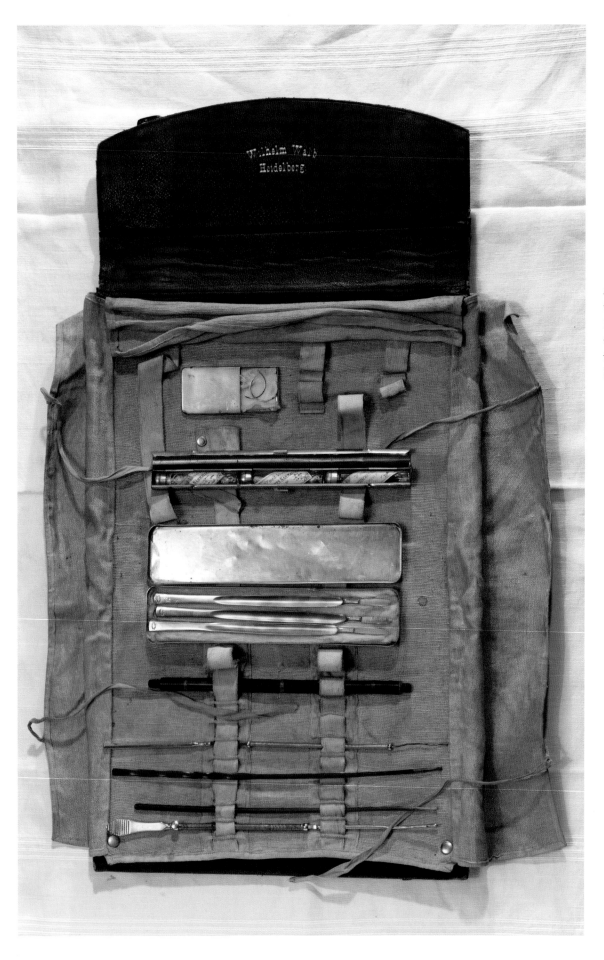

A traveling medical bag manufactured by Wilhelm Walb, late 1800s. Made in Heidelberg, Germany, this kit may be similar to one used by Dr. William Hillebrand.

to publish the names of delinquent subscribers. Arrangements were made with the minister of the interior to pay the hospital all amounts received from the passenger's and seamen's taxes, which would be used to care for sick and disabled seamen of vessels flying the Hawaiian flag. Finally, there were the important tasks of determining the plans and specifications for a hospital building and of finding a permanent site for The Queen's Hospital.

Early possible locations included a site adjoining the old city and county jail on Iwilei Road, or near the soap works on Palama Road, but the prevailing opinion was that the strong winds from Nuʻuanu Valley would be bad for patients. Another possible location was a one and a half acre lot at the head of Emma Street (now the corner of Emma and School streets). Finally, there was the nine-acre parcel at the corner of Punchbowl and Beretania Road. On January 5, 1860, the trustees selected the Punchbowl site, where Queen's stands today. The *Pacific Commercial Advertiser* had also campaigned for the site, suggesting that it was "conspicuous."[36] The hospital certainly would be prominently placed, but the vast area was also conspicuously vacant. Located past the edge of Honolulu, there was scarcely a building on the entire nine acres, and because of a lack of water it was barren—there were no trees, brush, or undergrowth. The American missionaries of Oʻahu, whose mission houses were located directly south of the parcel, would speak of visiting Lahaina, Maui, as a reprieve from the dry, dusty, and barren area in which they lived.[37]

Nevertheless, the trustees purchased the parcel for $2,000 from High Chief Kaisara (Caesar) K.K.K.K. Kapaʻakea[38] after determining that it would cost $700 to bring water to Beretania Road. The land was called Manamana, which means "branching," or "lots of *mana*" (spiritual power). Both meanings of the name have taken on significance as Queen's has grown over the past 150 years. The land came with a bonus: a two-story wooden structure that could be used for a temporary hospital during construction of a new building. It took five months to renovate the old wooden building and turn it into a twenty-four-bed hospital, and Dr. Hillebrand, his staff, and patients moved onto the Manamana property on March 10, 1860. Although the building was larger than the Thrum building, demand soon outstripped capacity. By June, Hillebrand reported that even the dining room and

dispensary were being used for patients. The Kapaʻakea structure served as a hospital for nine months.[39]

Determining the size of the new hospital building was no small decision. In February, the executive committee obtained bids for a building 40 by 82 feet, with estimates covering roughly each additional 10 feet up to a length of 120 feet. At first, a majority of trustees voted for a 120-foot building. Reconsidering, they chopped it to 100 feet, then increased it to 110. Four days later, they reconsidered and set the length back to 120. The apparent indecisiveness was due to finances. Although the executive committee had authorized a building contract for not more than $14,100, the treasurer's report showed assets of only $11,218. Two feet came off of the building's height, and a few days later, the length of the building was again cut back to 100 feet, and the total expense was limited to $13,500.[40]

Fortunately, the trustees had an architect to guide them through the process. Trustee Theodore Heuck, Hawaiʻi's first professional architect, showed the board how they could trim costs, then designed this first Queen's building without compensation. A native of Germany who arrived in Hawaiʻi in 1850, Heuck went on to design the Royal Mausoleum, ʻIolani Barracks, and other structures.[41] In spite of the deliberation and compromise, the final construction plans were announced to the public with the prediction that the hospital would be "the finest public building, as well as the most commodious for hospital purposes, that Honolulu will have to boast of for many years to come."[42]

Ground was broken on June 13, and the trustees set the date for the laying of the cornerstone for Saturday, July 14. However, the king was "attacked by the same fever from which Prince Lot is suffering," and the ceremony was postponed to Tuesday, July 17, 1860. At eleven o'clock that day a procession formed at Kawaiahaʻo Church and marched to the hospital grounds, which were described as "the foot of Punchbowl Hill." "It was a resplendent day here in Honolulu," the Hawaiian-language newspaper *Ka Hae Hawaiʻi* reported. "There were many *aliʻi*, legislators, and *haole*, as well as Hawaiians who joined in the march."[43] Queen Emma and her ladies in waiting were already at the hospital site, seated under a flower-trimmed canopy set up on the grounds. When the procession reached the grounds, the Reverend Armstrong gave a prayer in Hawaiian, and the Kawaiahaʻo choir stood to

Manamana, the land purchased from Chief Kapaʻakea, circa 1860. The new hospital building, designed by Theodore Heuck, sits prominently on the barren site; Kawaiahaʻo Church is in the distance at left. This view from Punchbowl shows the back of the hospital.

sing a hymn they had composed for the occasion. The king first gave a speech in Hawaiian as reported in *Ka Hae Hawaiʻi*. The speech reads in part (translated from Hawaiian):

What then are the feelings, and what is the manner of the sickness of those lacking basic necessities? Who do they yearn for when they are friendless?...They have no family, no friends, no house.... However, if a well meaning soul should extend a hand to a sick and troubled "Lazarus" lying at the doorway, and welcome him into his house,... and he revives from his illness, and he escapes death, what should be his payment? He has no money, nor wealth...

And thus we are all gathered here today....The Hawaiians are poor, they are sick, they are friendless. Here are their fortune—to be tended to until they are in good health....it is indeed proper for me this day to be the one to express publicly...the aloha of the people for this great blessing they have gained, and to show their appreciation to all those who have made donations, and assisted in this fine work, the building of The Queen's Hospital.[44]

The cornerstone consisted of two blocks of Waiʻanae sandstone. Sealed in the cornerstone was a copper box[45] containing ambrotypes (glass plate photographs) of the king and queen; a Hawaiian-language Bible; Books of Laws of the Nation; the newspapers *The Polynesian*, *Pacific Commercial Advertiser*, *Ka Hae Hawaiʻi*, and the *Friend*; the names of the administrators of the hospital; a copy of the charter and bylaws; and a list of the names of all contributors.

A Freemason proclaimed: "The Craftsmen having skillfully and faithfully performed their duty, in the name of the Fraternity of Free and Accepted Masons, I do solemnly declare this Corner Stone of The Queen's Hospital to be well formed, true and trusty." The chaplain of the Freemasons stood and said a prayer, and the men took in hand a square, plumb rule, and chisel. When it was certified that the stone was properly set, the king poured vases of corn, oil, and wine upon it—the Masonic symbols of life and the everlasting happiness of man.[46]

HALE MAʻI O KA WAHINE ALIʻI

King Kamehameha IV, circa 1855.
Daguerreotype by Benajah Jay Antrum.

The king then gave a different speech in English. It was said that his face came alive when he spoke of the hospital:

The Queen's Hospital, established for the relief and comfort of the indigent sick, has already taken its place among the prominent institutions of our country.... Contributions towards the support of a hospital, are declarations of kindness aforethought, and of a long-sighted policy of love towards those who need other hands than their own to smooth their restless pillows....

On an occasion such as this, it becomes me ... to express, in the name of my people, the sense of gratitude with which the liberality and fellow-feeling of those who helped to establish The Queen's Hospital have filled their hearts and mine.... In the name of the wretched and miserable, I thank you. In the name of the otherwise sleepless, I pray you may be at ease, and in the name of the dying, who die more painlessly for what you have done, I desire from the bottom of my heart, that long years of happiness may be in store for you.

But let me remind you that so long as sickness shall exist, there will be a duty imposed upon us.... Society makes distinctions broad enough, but strip us of our artificial robes, and we are one and all equally naked and equally exposed to the keen winds of want and the torments of disease. I trust, therefore, ... that you will continue your support to this praiseworthy institution.

... Particularly will you rejoice on this day which sees us met together to lay the corner stone of a building; which to yourselves will be an [sic] earnest of the permanency of the labor of love to which you have lent yourselves, while to a future generation it will be a monument to your memory, which will proclaim you for many years to come to have been, in your generation, benefactors of the human race.[47]

The king's speech "fell like dew on the hearts of the hearers." The audience was so rapt that one might have "heard the fall of a feather.... One gentleman (J. T. Waterhouse, Esq., a trustee) requested that his name might be entered for another One Hundred Dollars toward the support of the institution."[48]

Queen Emma, in the meantime, had been planning a fair to raise more funds.[49] *Ka Hae Hawai'i* reported in June that the queen planned "to get together the *haole* (foreign) women of Honolulu to put on an auction of precious things

as a fundraiser for this establishment of hers."[50] The queen knew that many women wanted to help but had no money, so she asked them to make fancywork and to prepare food to sell. Many women helped in other ways. Among the hospital's first volunteers, the ladies of Honolulu and their daughters hemmed sheets and made pillowcases for the patients.

The fair was held on November 29, 1860, a week before the new building opened for inspection. It took place at Armory Hall with delightful weather under what was called a well-filled moon. The crowded hall was bedecked with flags, flowers, and evergreens, decorated under the queen's supervision. Sales of baked goods were brisk, and the display of the women's "useful handiwork" lined tables on every side. The few articles left unsold were auctioned at the end. A total of $1,620.75 was raised at the fair, including the entry fee and sales.[51]

The extra funds were timely, for although the trustees had limited the total expense for the new building to no more than $13,500, the actual cost came to $14,728.92 ($301,938.73 in 2008 dollars).[52] Itemized costs included the amount of the contract, $11,400; prison labor, $702.65; hauling stone, $987.00; hauling sand, $18; cornerstone, $20; force pump, pipe, and digging well (not the artesian well, which was sunk in 1894), $189.64; painting, $816; paint, oil, lumber, and such, $353.65; lumber and carpenter's work, extra, $126.73; and mason's materials and labor, $115.25.[53]

On December 6, 1860, the completed hospital building was opened to the public for inspection. Furnishing took another week, and then The Queen's Hospital began admitting patients. The building was indeed heralded as one of the finest buildings in Honolulu, as the trustees boasted it would be. In 1936, on the 100th anniversary of Queen Emma's birthday, Dr. Nils Larson, the hospital's first medical director, wrote:

Thus in that city of less than 20,000; with King and Queen and House of Nobles; as well as House of Representatives; with its soldiers and its barracks; with drunken sailors and whalers; with missionaries trying to maintain the Christian ideals against the inroads of John Barleycorn and selfish commercial exploitation—a city then seemingly endlessly far from other centers of civilization, The Queen's Hospital was founded.[54]

Alexander Liholiho and Emma Nā'ea Rooke
around the time of their wedding on June 19, 1856.

KING KAMEHAMEHA IV AND QUEEN EMMA

Although the institutions and legacies of King Kamehameha IV and Queen Emma exist to this day, the glory years of their reign and marriage were short. Alexander Liholiho's reign lasted only nine years and his marriage to Queen Emma only seven—both were cut short by his untimely death in 1863 at twenty-nine years of age.

Born on January 2, 1836, Emma was the daughter of Pane (Fanny) Kekelaokalani Young and high chief George Nāʻea. Upon her birth, she was given to Fanny's sister, Grace Kamaʻikuʻi Young, and her husband, Dr. Thomas Charles Byde Rooke (1806–1858), under the longstanding Hawaiian custom of *hanai* (to adopt a child). Born in Hertford, England, Rooke earned his medical degree in 1826 and signed on as a surgeon on a whaling ship bound for the South Seas. He landed in Lahaina, Maui, in 1829. During his stay, Rooke befriended high chiefs and foreigners. When his ship docked at Honolulu Harbor after another whaling season, Rooke's friends persuaded him to stay and practice medicine. Described as "a man of rare cultivation and refinement" with a cheerful disposition, he endeared himself to the Hawaiians.[1] King Kamehameha III appointed him court physician. Rooke was so esteemed that an arrangement was made for him to marry Grace Kamaʻikuʻi Young, the second daughter of John Young, friend and counselor of Kamehameha I. Few foreigners at the time were allowed to marry a Hawaiian woman of *aliʻi* (royal) status.

Apparently unable to have children of their own, the Rookes arranged to adopt Emma before she was born. Grace also had a younger sister, Gini (Jane) Lahilahi, who had given her firstborn, Peter Kaʻeo, to their brother, John Kalaipaihala Young II (or Keoni Ana). Although still married to Joshua Kaeʻo, Jane later became the mistress of Kamehameha III. She bore him a son, Albert Kunuiakea, the cousin to whom Queen Emma willed a part of her estate.[2]

Known as a physician and surgeon of unusual skill, Dr. Rooke remained court physician until his death. He also maintained a dispensary at his home on the corner of Beretania Street and Nuʻuanu Avenue for natives who had no other access to medicine. Dr. Rooke was deeply devoted to Emma, who was a small, pretty child with delicate features. He raised her to be very British, while her adoptive mother had a strong Hawaiian influence and was prone to be more indulgent, especially because the child was considered royalty. It was this home environment that shaped Emma's British leanings, her passion for Western medicine, and her love for her people.

Emma grew up speaking both Hawaiian and English, the latter with a perfect British accent. She was bright, sensitive, and fun loving, but also could be stubborn. Her formal education began at age five at the Chiefs' Children's School. When the school closed in 1849, Dr. Rooke hired an English governess to tutor Emma for the next four years, but he also played an active role in her education. Emma learned a great deal about the outside world from her scholarly father, who assembled the finest library in Honolulu for her benefit. Rooke also taught Emma by example. Not only did he provide medical care to the poor, he also served as physician at the hospital for British Seamen, which was established in Pauoa Valley in 1846. In addition to being court physician, Rooke served as chamberlain, legislative representative, and member of the Privy Council at various times in his life. He was also one of the three commissioners appointed by Kamehameha III to control the spread of the smallpox epidemic in 1853. Rooke foreshadowed the establishment of The Queen's Hospital with his pleas in *The Polynesian* for the establishment of such an institution,[3] but he died suddenly at the age of fifty-two in 1858, when Emma was twenty-two years old.

Emma grew up to be an educated woman with good conversational skills and a love of gardening and music. She was known for her amiability, refined manners, and kind heart.[4] Most importantly, she was a passionate

Emma Nā'ea Rooke and her uncle, John Kalaipaihala Young II (Keoni Ana), circa 1850.

Dr. Gerritt P. Judd (center) with brothers Lot (left) and Alexander Liholiho (right), 1850.

believer in her father's lifelong efforts to bring medical care to those who needed it, and to establish a hospital. Two years before Rooke's death, Emma married Alexander Liholiho, who had become King Kamehameha IV in 1854.

Born on February 9, 1834 in Honolulu, Alexander 'Iolani Liholiho Keawenui had also been adopted under the custom of *hanai*. When Liholiho was born, his uncle, Kamehameha III, declared the child as his own and decreed that he would be heir to the throne. The grandson of Kamehameha I, Liholiho was born to Mataio Kekuanaoa, governor of Hawai'i, and Kīna'u, the *kuhina nui*, or prime minister, of the Kingdom of Hawai'i.[5] Liholiho's siblings included David Kamehameha, Moses Kekuaiwa, Lot Kapuāiwa, and Victoria Kamāmalu.

Liholiho attended the Chiefs' Children's School with Emma. Although his formal education was somewhat limited, Liholiho added to it by reading. Advisors to King Kamehameha III felt the heir to the throne would benefit from extensive travel, so, in 1849 when he was fifteen years of age, Alexander and his brother Lot accompanied Dr. Gerritt P. Judd on an official government trip to Paris, England, Washington DC, and numerous other places. Their mission was to negotiate a treaty between Hawai'i and France following the attack on Honolulu Fort by French Admiral de Tromelin.[6]

They sailed to San Francisco in 1849 and continued on to visit many European countries and met heads of state, including Louis-Napoléon Bonaparte (Napoléon III). In spite of a three-month stay in France, they failed to negotiate a treaty. However, in England they met Prince Albert (Queen Victoria was indisposed due to the imminent birth of her seventh child) and many other dignitaries. In America, Alexander was ill treated by a train conductor who almost threw him off a train because of the color of his skin, and by a butler who didn't want to serve "blacks." He called the experience with the conductor "the first time that I have ever received such treatment, not in England or France or anywhere else.... In England an African can pay his fare and sit alongside Queen Victoria. The Americans talk and think a great deal about their liberty, and strangers often find that too many liberties are taken of their comfort just because his hosts are a free people."[7] Many have concluded that Liholiho was anti-American. However, while it is true that he was a great admirer of English institutions and married a pro-

British woman in Emma, he also kept trusted American advisers. It does not appear that he was directly hostile to America; rather, it could be said that Liholiho was anti-missionary. Dr. G. P. Judd noted that the king most of all disliked the Mission, and that his heart was hardened to a degree unknown to the heathen.[8]

Liholiho was just shy of twenty-two years of age when he ascended the throne. Tall and slender, Liholiho was described by many as handsome. He was plagued by asthma, which often kept him from performing his public duties. To shore up his health, Liholiho once took boxing lessons from a pugilist called "Yankee Sullivan." He had an excellent mind, notable for breadth of knowledge and quick perception, rather than depth of knowledge.[9] Fluent in both Hawaiian and English, the new king was more European than Hawaiian, and was aristocratic, believing it was the duty of the upper class to govern the lower classes. Jules Remy, a French scholar who spent several years in Hawai'i during Liholiho's reign, noted that the king sometimes acted in an arbitrary or despotic way, and that he was passionate and quick-tempered, traits that would not serve him well. Remy also disclosed that the king had a tendency toward dissipation, keeping company with those who were far from role models. Despite these weaknesses, Liholiho was an active and responsible member of the Privy Council for three years before becoming king, and he took seriously his role in maintaining Hawai'i's independence while protecting the welfare of his people.[10]

Taking the advice of his trusted adviser and friend Robert Crichton Wyllie, Hawaiian minister of foreign affairs, the king decided (as Wyllie put it) to "marry and to give stability to the Throne by resorting to the ancient rule of Hereditary Descent."[11] That is, it was the king's responsibility to preserve the monarchy and maintain the Kamehameha line by having offspring. However, it was not only pragmatic duty that inspired the king. He and Emma had a deep affection for each other. In 1855, the king announced that they would marry. Not all the chiefs approved, among them High Chief Caesar Kapa'akea, who thought his daughter Lydia (the future Queen Lili'uokalani) would be a preferable choice.[12]

The wedding was held on June 19, 1856 at Kawaiaha'o Church with Church of England liturgy. The king and queen were favorites in Honolulu society, entertaining frequently

Portait of Prince Albert Edward Kauikeaouli Leiopapa a Kamehameha wearing his honorary fireman's suit, circa 1863.

and holding official receptions. On May 20, 1858 the queen gave birth to a son, Albert Edward Kauikeaouli Leiopapa a Kamehameha. There was great joy on behalf of the little prince, and the subjects of the kingdom pinned their hopes on the prospect that Albert would one day ascend the throne. Among his greatest admirers was R. C. Wyllie, who named his estate on Kaua'i "Princeville" in honor of Prince Albert. When they were apart, letters between the king and queen reveal the tender affection they had for each other and the little prince, whom they referred to as "baby."[13]

The young queen exerted a strong influence on the king to establish a hospital, although Liholiho was already interested in establishing one. However, on September 11, 1859, just over a month after The Queen's Hospital's temporary dispensary

Queen Emma, circa 1859.

passed though Neilson and miraculously did not kill him, but he remained in poor health for two and a half years until his death.[14]

The king discovered too late that his suspicions were unfounded. Filled with remorse, he decided to abdicate the throne. After two weeks of turmoil, the Privy Council unanimously passed a resolution protesting the king's abdication. Two days later, the king decided not to abdicate. He made amends as best he could by providing the best medical care he could offer to Neilson, as well as a letter of apology in which he called his action "this great false act of my life."[15] Bolstered by the support of the Privy Council and his supporters, the king was able to survive the crisis, but the psychological and emotional trauma were severe.[16]

By the time the Englishwoman Lady Franklin and her niece Sophia Cracroft visited the king and queen in April 1861, all seemed to have returned to normal, at least on the surface. Miss Cracroft called Queen Emma "rather good-looking" and wrote about her "fine eyes—brown complexion (a sort of chestnut colour), plenty of good hair, slightly wavy, a pretty nose and generally good features, with a stout and not very good figure."[17] At another time, she wrote that "the Queen is a sweet-mannered person, beloved by everyone, with excellent sense and charming simplicity." The king was "very cordial and unaffected. He is about the same shade of colour as the Queen, with fine wavy hair and good features, rather tall and not stout; his conversation was most agreeable. Both speak English perfectly, but with him it is more than fluency—he has evidently complete command of the language—and surrounded as he is by Americans … it is truly marvelous that he should have totally avoided their odious intonation." Of the little prince, now three years old, Miss Cracroft noted, "he is a sweet little boy, with his mother's pretty eyes, but fairer in complexion than either parent, and dark silky curls. He obeyed the order to shake hands with us with some shyness, but soon began to talk—English and Hawaiian are alike to him."[18]

Turning to his faith after the Neilson incident, the king assumed leadership in establishing the Anglican Church in Hawai'i, believing its doctrines and liturgy to be more compatible with the monarchy than the Congregational and Presbyterian churches.[19] He also began a translation of the *Book of Common Prayer* into Hawaiian. The king and queen's

opened, an incident involving the king almost derailed his reign. A large group that included the king, Queen Emma, and Prince Albert assembled to spend several weeks on the islands of Maui and Hawai'i. While on Maui, Liholiho's mind somehow became poisoned against a young American named Henry A. Neilson. A close friend of Liholiho from before he became king, Neilson served as his private secretary. The king let himself believe, or was led to believe, that his secretary had committed improprieties with the queen. In a jealous rage, he shot Neilson at close range. The bullet sponsorship of the Anglican Church in Hawai'i led to the founding of 'Iolani School in 1863.

In anticipation of Prince Albert's baptism, the king asked Queen Victoria to be Prince Albert's godmother. She sent a christening gift for her godson—a large, elaborate silver cup—with W. F. Synge, British commissioner and consul general to Hawai'i, who was expected to arrive in late August 1862. Meanwhile, Bishop Thomas Nettleship Staley prepared to leave England to establish the Anglican mission in the Kingdom of Hawai'i. He set sail on August 17. Upon his arrival, he was to baptize Prince Albert.

On August 19, the queen and the prince traveled to Waikīkī to visit Princess Bernice Pauahi Bishop and her husband, Charles Reed Bishop. That evening, the prince took ill, and the queen summoned a doctor. The next morning, she took the prince back to the palace and sent for the king. The doctors could not make a diagnosis. The *Pacific Commercial Advertiser* reported that the prince was suffering from an inflammation of the brain, but this was inaccurate.[20] The symptoms suggest that the prince was suffering from appendicitis, which was not curable in the 1860s. Synge arrived on August 22, not realizing the silver christening cup would rest near the prince at his funeral. Unable to wait for Bishop Staley, the Congregational minister of Kawaiaha'o Church was called in to perform Anglican baptismal rites on the 23rd, and on the morning of August 27, 1862, Prince Albert succumbed to his illness. The nation went into deep mourning, and the *Pacific Commercial Advertiser* stated, "The death of no other person could have been so severe a blow to the King and his people."[21]

Liholiho blamed himself for the death of his son, although there was nothing he could have done. Over the course of a year and until his death, the king did not seem well and kept out of the public eye as much as he could, although he managed to complete his translation of the *Book of Common Prayer*. His health was affected both by grief and chronic asthma, and perhaps other causes, but no one expected his early death on November 30, 1863.[22] Although Queen Emma was distraught, her faith carried her through the deaths of both her son and husband. In a letter to her attendant, Keli'imoewai, she wrote, "In my dreams last night, Alex came to me but looking so ill and poorly. He was very gentle and tender and oh it was [as] if of yore. Alas, I woke

to lose his presence. . . . Oh God's ways are mysterious and I must bear his decree." In another letter she wrote, "I am found under the shady koa of this place where the three of us dwelled. Then there were two of us, and now only I remain behind. But it is not for us to question God's ways."[23]

Queen Emma's humanitarian activities continued. She helped organize the Cathedral District Visiting Society, whose twenty volunteers visited the sick and the poor. As the leader of the group, the queen was the most frequent and devoted visitor of the needy. The society's services extended to the prison and The Queen's Hospital, where the queen was almost a daily visitor.[24] Keenly interested in the welfare and education of the young, she took many children under her wing. She helped found two schools, St. Cross in Lahaina, Maui, and St. Andrew's Priory in Honolulu. Traveling to England, Queen Emma enlisted the help of Queen Victoria and others to raise $30,000 for the construction of St. Andrew's Cathedral in Honolulu.

When King William Lunalilo—successor to Liholiho's brother, Lot Kapuāiwa (Kamehameha V)—died in 1874, he failed to name a successor, although there is evidence that his preference was for Queen Emma. However, since there was no official appointment, a monarch was required to be chosen among the *ali'i* by legislative ballot. Both Queen Emma and David Kalākaua campaigned. Although a sizable percentage of the native population supported Queen Emma, the representatives favored Kalākaua by thirty-nine to six. When the results of the ballot were announced, a small group of the queen's partisans incited a riot outside the courthouse, demolishing a carriage and using the pieces as clubs. The rioters smashed windows, destroyed furniture, and seriously wounded a few of the representatives; one later died of his injuries.[25]

Queen Emma remained interested in politics throughout her life, but did not attempt to run again. She continued her efforts to construct an Anglican cathedral and actively supported the St. Andrew's Priory and The Queen's Hospital. She tended her gardens alongside her gardeners, played tennis, and traveled on horseback, remaining active until her death in 1885 at age forty-nine.

MANAMANA

At the Foot of Punchbowl

A resident of Honolulu in the mid-1800s, Gorman D. Gilman described the area below Punchbowl this way: "A more forsaken, desolate looking place...can scarcely be imagined."[1] The Punchbowl site was considered on, but outside, the east boundary of Honolulu town. Had the trustees not been men of vision who saw the potential of the barren, waterless site called Manamana, The Queen's Hospital would likely have been quickly limited by its land.

Although there is no record of the early use of the land, the Hawaiians who lived in the area in the early 1800s described it as wasteland but built one or more houses for themselves.[2] Described as the foot of Punchbowl, the land gradually slopes toward the crater. That is why a person who enters the lobby of the modern Queen's and walks through the buildings to the back at Lusitana Street must catch an elevator to the third level to be at street level again.

The purchase of Kaisara (Caesar) Kapa'akea's property included nine acres; today, Queen's encompasses a whole city block, plus the Miller Street triangle, and covers about fifteen acres. Manamana actually belonged to Kapa'akea's wife, who was awarded the land during the Mahele—the division of lands in the mid-1800s that introduced the concept of private property into Hawaiian society. Properties were designated and recorded as Land Commission Awards (LCAs); many properties in Hawai'i are still identified as such. The nine-acre parcel the trustees purchased for $2,000 was a part of LCA 5874, *apana* (lot) 2, awarded to Analea Keohokālole, who was a high chiefess, daughter of 'Aikanaka and Kamae, and wife of Caesar Kapa'akea.[3] A subscriber to the hospital fund, Kapa'akea was a high *ali'i* (chiefly class), and great-grandson of Kame'eiamoku, one of the four chiefs who were instrumental in Kamehameha I's conquest of the Hawaiian Islands. Kapa'akea and his wife had four children, two of whom would become the Hawaiian monarchs King Kalākaua and Queen Lili'uokalani. Both were born on the property.

Kapa'akea's lot included most of the land fronting Punchbowl Street and the interior portion of the current city block. Property not included in the original purchase was a house lot (LCA 1818, *apana* 1) at the corner of Punchbowl and Beretania streets, which belonged to a woman named Kaiahua. The Mabel Smyth Memorial Building (now The Queen's Conference Center) is constructed on the site. The lot next to Kaiahua's property on Beretania was owned by Kuhia (LCA 656). The parcel next to Kuhia's belonged to John Papa 'I'i (LCA 268). 'I'i's property began at the corner of Beretania, where the Queen's Physicians' Office Building III is located today, and extended all along Lauhala Street. The son of a minor chief, 'I'i was a companion and personal attendant to the first Prince Liholiho, later King Kamehameha II. After the king's death, 'I'i continued to serve the *ali'i* and remained involved in the royal government. Crown lands were along Lusitana Street. Some of this land was leased by the Kapi'olani Estate. When the lease expired after 1912, the territorial governor promised to "set the land aside for public purpose, to wit, a hospital."[4] The hospital also purchased individual house lots, many along Miller Street, when they became available. All of these parcels contained within the city block eventually became a part of the Queen's campus.

Today, Beretania, Punchbowl, Miller, Lusitana, and Lauhala streets, along with Vineyard Boulevard, generally define the borders of the Queen's campus. Beretania Street, which means "Britain," was named for the British Consul Office located on this street in the 1800s. Punchbowl Road (now Street) was, of course, named after the extinct volcanic crater. Hawaiians called the crater Puowaina, which means "consecrated hill" or "hill of sacrifice." In ancient times, it was the site of secret *ali'i* burials, and offenders of certain *kapu*, or taboos, were sacrificed there. During the reign of Kamehameha I, two cannons mounted on the crater's rim saluted the arrival of distinguished people and marked important occasions. Miller Street was named after William Miller, consul general of Great Britain from 1844 to 1858,

Grounds of The Queen's Hospital lined with date palms, circa 1885.

left Pink bombax (*Pseudobombax ellipticum*) flowers. The pink
bombax tree on Queen's grounds was planted by Dr. William
Hillebrand in the late 1800s and is said to be the first one planted
in Hawai'i. The grounds also boast two white bombax trees.
Dr. Robert McKibbin Jr. continued the early efforts of Dr. William
Hillebrand to develop the landscaping of the hospital grounds.
In the 1870s, the board of trustees noted that the landscaping
of the grounds was "of as much importance in many respects
[to the well-being of the patients] as medical treatment itself."

opposite The Queen's Hospital, circa 1870s. Before the advent
of automobiles, visitors and staff could hitch their horses in front
of the hospital.

who lived between Miller Street and Washington Place.
Lusitana Street, which runs along the back part of the Queen's
campus, was named to honor the Portuguese Welfare Society, whose members, brought from the Azores as plantation
workers in 1883, built small, whitewashed houses on the
lower slopes of Punchbowl. Lusitana is a poetic name for
West Hispania, or Portugal.[5] Lauhala Lane (now Street),
which runs along the Waikīkī side of Queen's campus, is
the Hawaiian name for the pandanus leaf used in weaving.
Vineyard Street (now Boulevard) passed through the vine-
yards of the Spanish immigrant Don Francisco de Paula
Marin,[6] who not only introduced the grapes and other fruits
to Hawai'i, but was also Kamehameha I's business advisor,
bookkeeper, interpreter, sometime physician, and a captain
in the Hawaiian army.

Grass, shrubs, trees, and plants of any kind were badly
needed on the grounds. Not until 1861 was water piped in
from Pauoa Valley, as the trustees had envisioned. Queen's
sunk an artesian well on hospital premises in 1894 "for a sum
of $3,000." Although it was necessary to deepen the well in
1945,[7] Queen's obtains all of its water from this artesian well
to this day; city water would only be used in an emergency.

Queen's first physician, Dr. William Hillebrand, was
a noted botanist who collected rare seeds and plants from

abroad. Queen Emma gave him free reign with the land,
and many of the trees he planted still flourish. Three of the
trees planted by Hillebrand are classified as "exceptional"
by the City and County of Honolulu's County Arborist Ad-
visory Committee. One of the exceptional trees is the baobab
on Punchbowl Street near Miller. A native tree of Africa, it is
one of the largest, if not the largest, of its kind in the United
States, with a circumference of 18 feet, a height of about 50
feet, and a canopy of 72 feet. The second is the pink bombax,
said to be Queen Emma's favorite flower. Hillebrand's pink
bombax stands next to the porte cochere in front of the main
lobby. Originally from Mexico, the bombax blooms just once
a year on bare branches. Its large, brushlike flowers earned
it its common name: shaving brush tree. Considered medici-
nal, its bark was once used to soothe toothaches and harden
ailing gums. The third exceptional tree on Queen's campus
is the nawa, which is in front of the 'Iolani Wing. Indigenous
to Asia, the towering tree is the largest of its kind in the
United States. It is a member of the cocoa family and yields
karaya gum, which can be used as an adhesive agent in pill
making. Although not listed as exceptional, one of the largest trees at Queen's is the kapok, planted by Hillebrand in
1861. Commanding a central location on Queen's front lawn,
the immense shade tree is found in tropical Asia, Africa, and
America. Its seeds yield an oil that can be burned for light.[8]

In 1864, Dr. Hillebrand planted date palms along the
driveway leading up to the hospital building. The tradition
of planting stately palms has continued. Royal palms, introduced to Hawai'i by Hillebrand, currently grow in the Miller
triangle's green space, and loulu palms frame the front of the

Harkness Building courtyard. Monkeypod trees, also introduced to Hawai'i by Hillebrand, grow prominently on the Queen's campus. By 1871, the upper part of the lot was thickly planted with algeroba trees, and all the trees throughout the grounds were flourishing.[9]

After Dr. Hillebrand left the islands in 1871, his assistant, Dr. Robert McKibbin Jr., became head physician. McKibbin continued Hillebrand's interest in landscaping the grounds. A July 3, 1875 report by F. A. Schaefer, Esq., secretary of the board of trustees, noted:

Much care has been devoted to the Hospital grounds, for which Dr. R. McKibbin, Jr., deserves well merited thanks at the hands of the public. The variety of shade trees, of rare plants, vines, shrubs and flowers; the neatness and order of the entire surroundings, are essential requisites to a well appointed hospital and of as much importance in many respects as medical treatment itself.

The grounds in front of the hospital were used for parking even before the advent of automobiles, when visitors and staff needed a place to hitch their horses and park their carriages. In 1871, visitors could park horses, but grazing was not allowed. In 1902, the trustees resolved that "hitching posts [should] be placed in front of the Hospital, and some provision be made for sheltering the horses of the staff."[10] By 1909, it was suggested to the Visiting Committee that it would be advisable to erect a shed for autos. "It is damaging to varnish to leave a machine standing in sun and rain," the trustees said. "It is destructive to tires also. Several autos drawn up before the entrance to the Hospital constitute an obstruction to patients and visiting friends besides frightening the horses that have to come in the same way."[11] A new driveway was proposed in 1911 to "lessen the discomfort to patients from noise and fumes of carriages and motor cars."[12] In 1916, the superintendent was "instructed to take up the matter of the proper parking of automobiles in the Hospital

MANAMANA

The nawa is the most
prominent tree on
the 'Iolani Wing side
of Queen's front lawn.
Behind and to the left
is the kapok tree.

Punchbowl Street entrance to The Queen's Hospital, circa 1880s.

right Ricardo Madriaga, 1969.

grounds."[13] Today, cars still drive into the Queen's front area, but parking has been confined to garages. Even with four garages—the Physicians' Office Building I, II, and III garages and the Miller Street garage, totaling 2,606 parking spaces—parking is tight.

In 1890, a plot on hospital grounds was set aside for the cultivation of flowers at the request of the Reverend A. Mackintosh. This was the beginning of the Hospital Flower Society, started by Queen Lili'uokalani.[14] The chief work of its members was to bring a flower and a kind word weekly to each patient. In 1923, the society established the Social Services Department on a trial basis.[15] In 1949, it became a full-fledged department and today has grown to about fifty licensed social workers who work in every patient care area.

More recent contributions have been made to Queen's landscaping. In the 1930s, new varieties of cross-pollinated shower trees were planted around O'ahu. One of the varieties planted at Queen's became known as "Queen's Hospital White." The most recent landscaping of Queen's front lawn reintroduced this variety along Punchbowl Street. The tree has canary yellow blossoms that turn a creamy white at maturity. On his first day at work—June 6, 1947—Ricardo Madriaga planted a banyan sapling in front of the Mabel Smyth Memorial Building. He nurtured the tree for forty-two years until his retirement in 1989, when a brass plaque was mounted in his honor. Madriaga died in 2006, but the sprawling tree he planted lives on.[16]

Because the grounds are in the Capitol District of Honolulu, at least 40 percent of Queen's front area must remain open green space. Built in 1961, the State Capitol dictates the view plane through Punchbowl Crater. In addition to the front lawn landscaping, many indigenous Hawaiian plants have been planted between buildings and in courtyards throughout the campus.

Queen's original building, circa 1890. Trade winds kept the hospital cool, and Punchbowl Crater was thought to shelter it from Nu'uanu Valley's strong winds. Designed by Theodore Heuck in 1860, the building had deep verandas, a ventilated skylight, and double rows of adjustable ventilators at floor and ceiling levels to "purify and constantly admit fresh air." By the 1890s, sections of the verandas were being enclosed, as seen in this photograph.

ESTABLISHMENT AND GROWTH

1860–1900

From a distance, the original Queen's building must have looked small and lonely sitting on nine acres of land, but it was imposing and handsome upon approach, and was one of the finest buildings in Honolulu. The entry was from Punchbowl Street, just as it is today. The orientation of the present-day lobby is exactly the same as the 1860 building, and it occupies almost the same spot.

There were actually four buildings on the premises in 1860—the wooden Kapaʻakea building in front (demolished in 1864), and two outbuildings in the rear (a substantial cookhouse of stone connected to storerooms, servants' rooms, and a wash house), and stables. The Englishwoman Sophia Cracroft—who had accompanied her aunt, Lady Franklin, on a trip to Hawaiʻi—described a visit to the hospital with Queen Emma just four months after it began accepting patients:

We drove first to the "Queen's Hospital," as it is called, on account of her [Queen Emma's] great interest in its erection and welfare. It ... is the first institution of the kind in the Kingdom, beyond small buildings to receive foreign sailors who fall sick. ... There was nothing whatever for the natives, and so strong were their prejudices against a hospital that very many were persuaded they could never be overcome ...

The building lies just out of town ... under the remarkable hill called the Punchbowl. It is constructed of coral blocks, covered with stucco, and is surrounded on the lower floor by a deep verandah, above which is another upon which the rooms on the upper story all open—most charming, but absolutely necessary adjuncts in a hot climate. It has a flat roof, graveled, and guarded by a high parapet.

There are about 40 persons now here—several for internal abscesses and tumours (a very common complaint), two for blindness having been already corrected. All were Hawaiians, pure or half-caste—apparently equal numbers of men and women. It is under the charge of Dr. Hillebrand, a clever and interesting person ... who has but four assistants for the conduct of the establishment: namely a dispenser (the only European: he is a Portuguese), a cook, and two other native attendants. The furniture and appointments are of the very simplest kind and smallest quantity. ... All was perfectly clean, well ventilated, and orderly.[1]

A Look Inside the New Hospital

The main building was 100 by 48 feet. The first floor was raised on a basement about 5 feet off the ground. To enter, a visitor ascended a broad flight of stairs to the veranda, which was 10 feet deep and ran the full length of the building. The double front doors opened into a hall about 25 feet wide, at the back of which was the main staircase. The ceilings were high—13 feet on the first floor and eleven on the second. The inner walls were plastered on both sides, "making a dry, healthy and substantial finish."[2] To the left was the Reception Room. Occupying the left front corner of the first floor was a dispensary accessible both from the interior and from the veranda, where patients waited for medications. Patients exited the dispensary from a door on the side of the building. On the right side of the first floor was a patient ward with two rows of seven parallel beds with bathrooms at the end.

An 8-foot-wide corridor ran lengthwise through the middle of the first floor. Two extra flights of stairs from each end of this corridor led to the second level, providing the upper wards easy access to the dispensary. Behind the first floor corridor were two large wards with a dining room in the middle. The second story also had a subdividing corridor, and there were five wards with varying capacities and a dining room.

Hawaiʻi's trade winds kept the hospital cool, and Punchbowl Crater was thought to shelter it from Nuʻuanu Valley's strong winds. To "purify and constantly admit fresh air," there were double rows of ventilators near the floor and ceiling, regulated by sliding covers. In the center of the

The Queen's Hospital, circa 1880. The original 1860 building designed by Theodore Heuck is to the far right. Three other buildings were also built around this time: the foreigners' ward (1877), "a new brick building" (1881), and the Bishop Wing (1893). The two prominent buildings here may be the foreigners' ward and the 1881 brick building.

building over the main staircase was a large raised skylight with ventilation around it, sitting on a flat roof finished with a "new asphaltic patent composition." In conjunction with the other ventilation in the building, this was thought to provide "light and pure air...gained without exposing the patients in any way...to drafts...disagreeable and dangerous."[3] Credit was given to T. C. Heuck not only for designing the building but also for devising "the first introduction of systemic ventilation."[4]

The Hawaiian people must have been awed by the imposing but magnificent hospital built for them by their *aliʻi*. Although not overly ornate, it was one of the few stone buildings in Honolulu at the time. Yet, many Hawaiians must also have looked upon the building with trepidation. They remembered all too well the *hale make* (houses of death) they had been forced to enter during the smallpox epidemic seven years earlier. Foreigners called them pest houses or hospitals, and they were supposedly for the good of the Hawaiians, but most who entered never returned home, and the foreigners did not set foot in them. In spite of their fears, they came for the sake of their beloved Queen Emma.[5] Sophia Cracroft sheds light on Queen Emma's role:

The Queen's manner was excessively pleasing. She recognized two or three of the patients and spoke to them (as she did also to some whom she did not know) with so much simple cordiality that it did one good to see her. . . . On going away, we saw ample proof that the former prejudices against a hospital were fading away, in the large number of out-patients waiting to see Dr. Hillebrand.[6]

Because there was no budget to hire trained nurses, Dr. Hillebrand relied on *kokua*, or helpers. The hospital's floor plan speaks of orderly rows of beds, but one who walked through the wooden floored wards would have also seen patients on their straw mattresses and pillows, some choosing to sleep behind mosquito netting, and *kokua*, with their sleeping mats on the floor between the beds. Although the hospital was described as clean and orderly, it would have been flush with humanity.

A patient's *kokua* could be a mother, sibling, aunt, close family member, friend, or servant. Some patients hired "watchers." Patient rates were usually qualified by the phrase "wine and watchers extra," indicating that the rates for pay patients did not include someone to look after you at all times—or your wine. A room was set aside for *kokua* to store their supplies and cook meals. They helped with the laundry, which was a very time-consuming task without modern detergents or equipment. Others performed the daily cleaning of the wards. *Kokua* would provide all nursing care at The Queen's Hospital for twenty-six years, until the first trained nurse was hired in 1886.

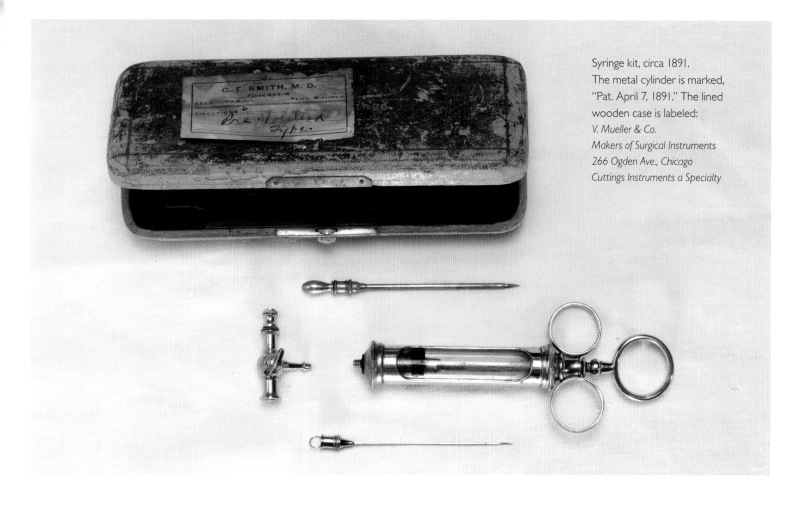

Syringe kit, circa 1891.
The metal cylinder is marked,
"Pat. April 7, 1891." The lined
wooden case is labeled:
V. Mueller & Co.
Makers of Surgical Instruments
266 Ogden Ave., Chicago
Cuttings Instruments a Specialty

Bladder cannula kit, made by Josef Leiter, Vienna, circa early 1900s. The instruments were used to inflate or drain bladders. The bottom drawer is steel-lined to store soiled instruments.

Those who visited generally observed that the hospital had a strict regard for cleanliness, but sanitation was difficult in the nineteenth century. The first sections of Honolulu's sewer system were not installed until 1889, and cesspools were used for most homes and buildings. Many modern innovations in plumbing were yet to be devised. Although the hospital was among the first places in Hawai'i to install flush toilets, early versions were not efficient in dispensing with solid waste. It wasn't until the late nineteenth century that efficient, siphon toilets were developed. An inspection ordered by the trustees in 1887 to discover the source of an outbreak of typhoid fever in the hospital revealed plumbing problems. Bathrooms were described as exceedingly foul. The cesspool, located "not a hundred feet from the south corner of the main building," was overflowing and imperfectly covered, and the report recommended moving it to a far corner of the property.[7]

Patients were placed in wards by race (generally) and gender, not by medical condition or age. Hawaiians were placed in "native wards," and foreigners had their wards. One reason given for this arrangement is offered in a 1907 Visiting Committee report: "We are satisfied that the Superintendent does his best to assign patients to those wards which they will find most congenial. We believe that the aim is to segregate patients according to habits—not race."[8] Perspectives on race varied. King Kamehameha IV supported the importation of foreigners to boost the native population by intermarriage. After noting that the "Chinese coolie immigrants, to whom has been given a trial of sufficient length," did not meet up with expectations and seemed to "have no affinities, attractions or tendencies to blend with this, or any other race," the king endorsed bringing in "the inhabitants of other Polynesian groups" who might more easily acclimate to the culture of Hawai'i. "Such immigrants," he said, "would pave the way for a future population of native-born Hawaiians."[9] Hawai'i had not yet earned its reputation as a melting pot.

The Practice of Medicine at The Queen's Hospital

Strong evidence for the infectious nature of diseases was identified as early as 1795, but the prevailing theory in the latter half of the nineteenth century held that disease was caused by an imbalance of the "four humours"—that is, the excess or deficiency of blood, phlegm, yellow bile, and black bile. The doctor's job was to identify the imbalances unique to each patient. Imbalances, it was thought, were caused by inhospitable climates, overcrowding, or miasmatic (bad) air. The main treatment for these imbalances was bloodletting.

Although slow to be accepted in the United States, germ theory was readily accepted in Hawai'i as early as 1882 with an understanding of the role of germs in leprosy.[10] An 1884 report noted that "parasitic germs" were found in patients with tuberculosis, gonorrhea, pneumonia, and leprosy.[11] A vaccine was available to control smallpox, but other infectious diseases such as typhoid fever, diphtheria, syphilis, and tuberculosis went unchecked. The hospital was not equipped to handle people with infectious diseases, nor those with mental disorders or drug addictions. Therefore, Queen's doctors in the nineteenth and early twentieth centuries adhered to a list of debarred diseases. Those who had a debarred disease were generally denied admission.

It was the duty of the Board of Health to care for people with infectious diseases in sanitariums, although friction with Queen's over accepting them occurred. "Incurable" diseases were also problematic. Unlike communicable diseases from which recovery or death was in a matter of days or weeks, incurable diseases could last for months or years. The hospital could not allow its limited number of beds to be filled with "incurables." In 1866, those who contracted leprosy, or Hansen's disease, were exiled to Kalaupapa, Moloka'i. Also in 1866, the O'ahu Insane Asylum was built to care for the mentally ill, rather than confining them to prison as had been the practice. The Honolulu Home for the Incurables—later called Leahi Hospital—was established in 1901 for those afflicted with a variety of diseases, but later became a hospital for tuberculosis patients.

In 1861, Hawai'i faced a measles epidemic. The question of whether to allow people with measles into the hospital immediately arose, and a special meeting of the trustees was called. With no cure for infectious diseases, the focus was on keeping patients in the hospital safe from infection. The fact that the issue was debated suggests that in 1861, Hillebrand may have been forward thinking with regard to the contagious nature of diseases. However, he felt those with measles should be admitted, reasoning that it would be impossible to keep the disease out of the hospital anyway. A special ward was kept for measles patients during the three-month epidemic.[12]

Another admissions issue surfaced in 1861. The trustees received a request from the minister of the interior (Prince Lot) to admit prostitutes. The request stemmed from a series of acts approved by King Kamehameha IV to suppress prostitution in 1855 and culminating in "An Act to Mitigate the Evils and Diseases Arising from Prostitution" in 1860.[13] Venereal diseases were causing the deaths of thousands of Hawaiians. Because it was impossible to stamp out prostitution, the legislature and the king sought to regulate it by requiring prostitutes to register with the sheriff and be regularly examined by a doctor.[14] Those who were found to be diseased would receive free treatment. The Kingdom looked to The Queen's Hospital to care for these women.

The trustees' decision to formally admit women to The Queen's Hospital in 1859 had paved the way for the admission of prostitutes.[15] They agreed that, beginning November 1, 1860, the hospital would treat prostitutes at a rate of 45 cents a day. However, a group of thirty-four Honolulu women protested that nothing should be done to lessen the "shame and ignominy which it is so desirable should be attached to those who have voluntarily and openly chosen the path of vice."[16] The trustees responded that the hospital had been established for the benefit of the nation, not for any particular class of patients or diseases—nor should it withhold care because of how a patient contracted a disease. The Kapaʻakea building was ideally suited for the prostitutes since it had been abandoned when the hospital building was completed.

From October 1860 through December 1861, 512 women were examined. Of those, 207 were infected with venereal disease; twenty-five were admitted, and 182 were treated at the dispensary. "The number of diseased are regularly diminishing," reported Dr. Robert McKibbin Jr., the attending government physician, "and in opposition to the prognostications of those who would rather leave the unfortunate to die in their sins without giving a chance of amendment, the law is showing its beneficial effects to the satisfaction of all who can sympathize with misfortune, even when associated with crime."[17]

However, in 1872 and 1873, The Queen's Hospital began to report dramatic increases in syphilitic cases after the "Act to Mitigate" was repealed.[18] The only treatment available at the time used toxic mercury compounds. Discovered in 1909, Salvarsan had much better, but still limited, success against syphilis. Hospital documents show that the use of Salvarsan was well established at Queen's in 1912, but neither syphilis nor gonorrhea could be easily cured until the advent of antibiotics in the 1940s.

Navigation through Difficult Times

The years immediately following the founding of The Queen's Hospital were marred by tragic deaths and financial troubles. A distraught Queen Emma took the name Kaleleonalani (the flight of the heavenly chiefs) after the deaths of both Prince Albert and Liholiho. Prince Lot Liholiho Kapuāiwa, Alexander Liholiho's brother, was proclaimed King Kamehameha V. Prince Lot had served as minister of the interior from 1857 to 1863 before ascending the throne as Kamehameha V. Besides being president of The Queen's Hospital Corporation, his major health initiative was the isolation and treatment of leprosy. During the second year of his reign, he signed the Segregation Act, which established a receiving hospital in lower Kalihi and sent patients to Kalaupapa, Molokaʻi, in 1866.

Dr. F. L. Miner's ebony, ivory, and platinum cauterization kit (De Paquelin Thermo-Cautére, Mon Charriére Collin, Paris, late 1800s). Dr. Claude André Paquelin invented this apparatus, which included small alcohol and gasoline burners to heat a platinum cauterization tip at a controlled temperature.

opposite

Wooden homeopathic medicine kit with slots for fifty-four vials, 1800s. A handwritten inventory of vial contents is included.

Although The Queen's Hospital had received much fanfare when its new building opened in 1860, keeping the hospital open was an ongoing financial challenge. Because most of the patients were nonpaying in the beginning, the trustees were relentless in seeking out new sources of funding. The only regular income was from government appropriations, taxes, and Board of Health funding, a total of about $342 a month. Operating expenses were about $500, leaving a deficit of approximately $158 a month. The trustees pursued commitments from foreign governments for the care of their respective seamen, but this proved to be slow and difficult. They had better success in appealing to consular patients—ailing foreigners placed in the hospital by various diplomatic agents. Churches were asked to take a special collection for the hospital, but only $276.53 was collected. Pressure was also put on subscribers who had not yet paid their pledges. Other sources of income were the legislature and private pay patients. The appropriations bills of 1860 and 1861 provided an annual cash grant of $2,000. The trustees also formed a committee to determine a weekly rate for "private persons" to be received for room, board, and medical care.

In spite of these difficulties, *The Polynesian* wrote that although "native prejudices against foreign doctors and foreign medicine were nearly as great two years ago, yet . . . new applicants throng to be received, and they gladly come from the remotest corners of the Kingdom to partake of the healing influences of this institution."[19] After three years as Queen's physician, Dr. Hillebrand stated that over 6,000 people had applied for treatment at the hospital, and 612 patients, including ninety-two foreigners, had been admitted. In addition, more than 16,000 prescriptions were supplied. By June 1869, F. A. Schaefer, secretary of the board of trustees, reported that "2,384 patients have been received into the Hospital, *viz*: 2,055 natives, and 329 foreigners; 309 deaths have occurred of which 245 were among the native and 63 among the foreign patients; 65,111 prescriptions stand on the books, but the real number . . . is much higher, as repetitions . . . are seldom set down."[20]

A Quick Succession of Kings

On December 11, 1872 the Kamehameha dynasty came to an end with the death of King Kamehameha V. Early in 1873, the highest surviving chief, William Lunalilo, was elected king by the legislature, but only reigned until December of that year when he succumbed to tuberculosis. Lunalilo took an active interest in The Queen's Hospital. A report by F. A. Schaefer commended his repeated visits, opining that the king's "close inquiries into the individual cases of his suffering subjects will cheer them, and assure them that the Hospital deserves the confidence, support, and care of the nation."[21] Lunalilo left no successor, so a legislative election was held. After defeating the dowager Queen Emma in a bitter election, David Kalākaua succeeded Lunalilo in 1874.

Increased Demand and a Changing Hawai'i

By 1873, the hospital was overcrowded. Dr. McKibbin Jr. reported that the number of patients accommodated in the first three months of the year was the largest ever. At the end of March, there were ninety-six patients in the hospital: fifty males and thirty-seven females (Hawaiian), and nine foreigners, all males. A report later in the year stated, "There are ninety-one patients, every bed being occupied, and in some instances, two males have to sleep together, owing to the large number of patients in the institution."[22] Although the hospital was originally intended to accommodate 124 patients, Heuck's floor plan shows only 112 beds. Perhaps the number of beds was reduced when the trustees shortened the length of the building from 120 to 100 feet. It is also possible that there were space issues not accounted for in the original design. Also, because different classes of patients were kept separately, some wards may have had vacant beds.

In spite of the overcrowding, the hospital ran a deficit during 1872 and 1873 and didn't appear to be in a financial position to expand. At the end of 1872, liabilities, including wages, "provisions, medicines, bedding, furniture, fuel, lights, washing, coffins, *etc.*," totaled $3,411.91, while assets, including pay patients, the passengers' and Hawaiian seamen's taxes, and appropriations, amounted to only $1,023.62, leaving a deficit of $2,388.29.[23] In 1874, however, finances began to turn around, and the hospital had a balance of $1,000.83 and no debts.[24] The following year, the cash on hand rose to $2,626.80.[25] Income from the seamen's and passenger's taxes had been steadily rising due to increased travel to Hawai'i. Increased payments from the Interior Department and from pay patients also helped put the hospital in a much better financial condition by its twentieth anniversary in 1879.

As the hospital's financial picture improved, the trustees did not hesitate to expand. Although the first new building is often thought of as the Bishop Wing, a number of apparently unnamed buildings were constructed before it. In 1877, a two-story, wooden building was erected "north of the main structure [Miller Street side] . . . containing wards, dining room, *etc.* for foreign patients," and a new dining room was added on the south end of the main building, all at a cost of $5,282.[26] The new building for foreigners was to the left of the original building and ran back toward Miller Street.

The new foreigners' ward was built to anticipate growth, but the trustees did not feel it would be adequate. In the Biennial Report of 1877–79, it was pointed out that "the great

Native Hawaiians at the hospital entrance, 1890. In the late nineteenth century, the developing agriculture industry resulted in an influx of immigrants. Plantation workers and their descendants would change the demographics of the patient population of Queen's.

influx of Chinese laborers during these two years, subject to hospital tax cannot possibly continue for a length of time, and if the number of foreign patients of the Hospital should still increase, the accommodations for them will have to be enlarged and at no small cost."[27] During the period from 1879 to 1881, 568 Hawaiians and 394 foreigners were treated— showing a marked increase in foreign patients; "out-door," or dispensary patients, totaled 5,380. By July 7, 1881, a new

ESTABLISHMENT AND GROWTH

View of Honolulu from
Punchbowl Crater, 1894.
At left is the back of The Queen's
Hospital buildings. Rows of royal
palms indicate the driveway leading to the main entrance of the
hospital.

brick building was also erected. John H. Paty, secretary pro tem, reported:

The Hospital can now comfortably lodge 120 patients. The cost of the new brick wing was originally $6,850, since when some few hundred dollars have been expended in alterations and additions thereto. It contains a spacious dispensary, and a well lighted operating room, with a fine dining room, a sick ward, and two convenient storerooms on the ground floor. On the second floor are two light and airy wards, and the Purveyor's quarters.[28]

Other accommodations were also added:

A small building with two rooms, for persons afflicted with offensive diseases, cost $150, the labor being done by some of the inmates; In place of the long, low shed (which was actually tumbling down) occupied as a dead-house, carpenter and paint shops and originally built of old material, a new structure measuring 80 x 15 feet, with ample space for all purposes required, has just been completed at a cost of about $600.[29]

The same report states that "the main building has been thoroughly repainted" with paints and oils, "which has been put on mostly by the patients and employees."[30] Patients also made sheets, pillowcases, and mosquito nets for the beds.[31] At least as of 1904, a hospital circular issued by management stated that "when extra attendants are required, convalescents are employed as far as possible, at the rate of 50 cents a day and 50 cents per night."[32]

Meanwhile, the duties of the purveyor were increasing, and the job title was changed to "superintendent" in 1894 to reflect this. The superintendent's duties included those of bookkeeper, commissary (he purchased bedding, meat, fish, poi and other groceries, and every other type of supply), apothecary (he prepared prescriptions ordered by the doctors), anesthetist, surgical assistant, and head nurse.[33] He also served as head administrator of the hospital; as such he was in charge of staff issues and reported directly to the trustees. An account by Jose Passos Rodrigues, purveyor from 1879 to 1882, sheds light on life at the hospital during this period. Part of his job "was to get the patients drunk, so they would not feel the pain so much, as we lacked anesthetics in those days." Rodrigues continued, "It was easy to get the Hawaiians drunk, as the law prohibited them from

using liquor at that time."[34] Ether was first used as an anesthetic for general surgery in 1842, and news of this innovation reached Hawai'i in 1847, so it is not clear why the hospital would lack it thirty years later. However, medications came all the way from London, which took six months; perhaps there was some disruption in the supply of ether during Rodrigues's tenure at Queen's.

Rodrigues's account also describes the 1877 foreigners' ward: "The other building near Miller street, a two-story one, built with red wood, was erected for the white people. Down stairs was one large ward, and up stairs, private rooms. When I started to work for the hospital in 1879, the place was not even painted; perhaps through lack of finance."[35] His description continues:

When the cannon were fired off from Punchbowl hill, as a salute for King Kamehameha and King Kalakaua's birthday… the concussion was so great that the building shook from the vibration of the loud reports, and plaster fell from the wall of the building in places. Shortly after that the cannon were removed to Waikiki at Prince Kuhio's place.[36]

Leaving his position at Queen's to become Honolulu's first tailor, the profession for which he was trained, Rodrigues went on to design most of King Kalākaua's clothing. Rodrigues noted that after he left, his brother-in-law, "John F. Eckardt," took his place. Johannes Eckardt was the superintendent at Queen's for over thirty years.

In 1883, the Visiting Committee reported a falling off in attendance—and a consequent decrease of receipts. The trustees attributed this to the presence of more government physicians on the other islands and the advent of steam transport, which allowed the U.S. Consulate to send sailors to the marine hospital in San Francisco. There was also a decrease in the regular and prolonged attendance of native women. But most significantly, increasing numbers of plantations were providing medical care.

The developing agricultural industry in Hawai'i depended on an adequate labor force. Because of the disastrous decline in the native population, there was great need for foreign workers. Large influxes of immigrant groups eventually forced the Hawaiian government to establish policies regarding their treatment, including providing medical care.[37] The first contract labor came from China in 1852. Portuguese laborers followed in 1878, and Japanese contract laborers came by large shiploads in 1885. The Japanese were followed by laborers from Spain, Germany, and Sweden. After 1900, Koreans and Filipinos followed. The growth of plantation medicine and hospitals did not after all threaten The Queen's Hospital's census, for a new wing was necessary by 1893. Rather, plantation medicine would become a part of the matrix of medical care in Hawai'i for nearly a century—one in which Queen's would play an important role. Plantation workers and their descendants would change the demographics of the patient population of Queen's and the cultural fabric of Hawai'i.

The Heavenward Flight of Emma Kaleleonalani

Queen Emma had never been seriously ill until 1883, when it appears that she had a small stroke. She was able to continue her charitable work, but the next year she had a more serious stroke while visiting Kohala on the island of Hawai'i. Emma was said to be recovering and appeared to be in reasonably good health well into 1885, but she died in April of that year at forty-nine years of age. Emma's obituary describes her death:

On April 24th, she complained of a headache, and Dr. McKibbin prescribed remedies. The next morning she felt better but complained of a feeling of heaviness. At ten minutes to one the doctor was summoned in haste—the Queen had had a slight convulsion. When Dr. Trousseau arrived the Queen was nearly pulseless. She was brought around by Drs. McKibbin and Trousseau, but after two more attacks, they were unable to help her, and the gentle spirit burst from its earthly bonds. In one short hour from the time the physician was summoned, the Queen had breathed her last.[38]

An Eventful Close of the Century

The end of the nineteenth century was tumultuous in Hawai'i's history. Electricity arrived in Honolulu in 1886. A large fire consumed Chinatown in downtown Honolulu that year. In 1887, King Kalākaua was forced to sign the "Bayonet Constitution," creating a constitutional monarchy, stripping the king of most of his power, and transferring it to the legislature, which was controlled by American, European, and Hawaiian power brokers. King Kalākaua died from pneumonia in late 1891, and his sister, Queen Lili'uokalani, assumed the throne. Lili'uokalani attempted to

The Estate of Queen Emma Kaleleonalani

Emma signed her will on October 21, 1884 after recovering from her second stroke. Her estate would have longstanding ramifications for The Queen's Hospital. Emma bequeathed money and property to various individuals, and the remainder of her landholdings were put in trusts for her cousin Albert Kunuiakea and Alexander Cartwright, her business agent.

The earnings from the landholdings bequeathed to Kunuiakea were to provide income for him for life. At his death, his children or grandchildren would receive title to the lands. However, if he died without descendants, The Queen's Hospital would receive these lands.[39] As it turned out, Kunuiakea died childless in 1903, and the hospital became the beneficiary of his portion of Emma's estate. The queen did not direct how her lands or income from the lands should be used by the hospital.

Cartwright received no personal benefit from his portion of the trust lands. The income from these trust properties were to pay four annual annuities (to certain individuals) and provide the St. Andrew's Priory with $600 per year for four scholarships of $150 each (called the Queen Emma Scholarships). The four annuities and scholarships, totaling $2,700 annually, were a first charge on income from the land held in trust. The remainder of the income, if any, would be divided equally between Kunuiakea and The Queen's Hospital. When Kunuiakea died, the hospital received his share of the income. When the last annuitant died in 1928, the trust was kept only to protect the interests of the $600 in scholarships. These lands, located in Hālawa, Waikīkī, and downtown Honolulu, became the most valuable of Emma's estate, but in 1884, the properties were worth only a fraction of what they would be later. In 1908, these lands were valued at just $68,000 and yielded only about $5,000 in revenues, so the trust was justified. By 1949, however, the properties were worth about $1 million and yielded $50,000 of income. In 1950, the Queen Emma lands were turned over to The Queen's Hospital by court order, reserving only a small parcel of real estate (two downtown Honolulu lots) to secure the scholarships.[40] While Queen's received a relatively small amount from the estate prior to 1950, it would benefit thereafter from increased amounts, which would be used to fund new buildings.

Much of the land remained under long-term leases until 1967, when the Queen Emma trust was abolished and the two downtown lots were turned over to Queen's. In return, Queen's agreed to give St. Andrew's Priory a gift of $25,000 to assure continuance of the scholarships. The Priory was "more than happy" with the settlement, since even a modest return on the $25,000 would almost double what the school had received before.[41] The four scholarships are still in existence today. Income from the Queen Emma lands continues to be a significant source of funds for new construction, renovations, and community health programs.

Queen's Nurses' Home, circa 1898.

abrogate the 1887 constitution and substitute one that would restore power to the monarchy. The queen was deposed on January 17, 1893, and a provisional government of American and European businessmen was established. The following year, the Republic of Hawai'i was established. An 1895 counterrevolution was attempted to overthrow the republic and reinstate Queen Lili'uokalani. During a gun battle near Diamond Head, Charles L. Carter, a Queen's trustee and supporter of the government, was shot three times in the chest and died later in the day. The Queen's Hospital went about its business of providing hospital care. The change in government was duly noted by a proposal to amend the by-laws of The Queen's Hospital Corporation: the phrase "His Majesty the King" would be struck wherever it appeared and substituted with "the Minister of the Interior."[42] On August 12, 1898, Hawai'i was annexed to the United States.

Disease did not take a break from afflicting the people of Hawai'i. Attention was diverted from politics when cholera broke out among Chinese immigrants who arrived on August 9, 1895 on the steamer *Belgic*, out of Yokohama, Japan. There were eighty-seven cases and sixty-four deaths during the epidemic, including several nurses who cared for the patients. The 1896 census revealed the changing population of Hawai'i. There were 16,399 Hawaiians, 22,329 Japanese, and 19,382 Chinese.[43] The combined total of Americans, British, German, French, Portuguese, and Norwegians was 13,361.[44]

Queen's Staff Expands

In the early years, the staff of The Queen's Hospital grew slowly. In 1869, Dr. Robert McKibbin Jr. was appointed to help Hillebrand as assistant physician at $600 a year. He succeeded Hillebrand as physician-in-charge when the German doctor left the islands in 1871. Dr. Clifford Brown Wood began his association with Queen's in 1888, when there were only two doctors in charge of the hospital, Dr. McKibbin Jr. as chief physician, and Dr. Brodie as assistant physician. When Brodie resigned in 1891, Wood took his place. When McKibbin resigned shortly after, the trustees created a new division of duties by separating the medical and surgical departments. Wood became Queen's first attending surgeon in 1892.[45] The first trained nurse was hired in 1886 at $500 a year. The first graduate nurses in Hawai'i came to work at Queen's in 1892, and not until that year were outside doctors allowed to practice medicine at the hospital. Any physician resident of Honolulu and licensed to practice in Hawai'i could apply for appointment on Queen's Honorary Board of Physicians. Appointees received the privilege of practicing in the hospital, and the regular attending staff was chosen from them each year.

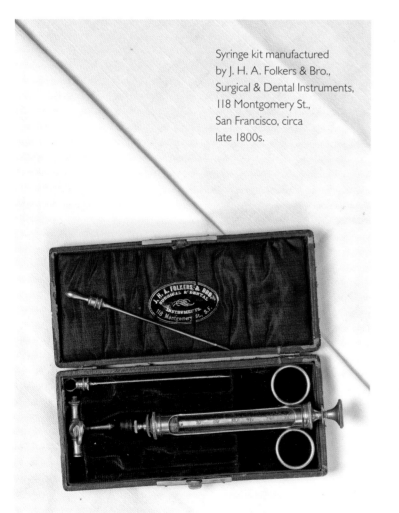

Syringe kit manufactured by J. H. A. Folkers & Bro., Surgical & Dental Instruments, 118 Montgomery St., San Francisco, circa late 1800s.

The Bishop Wing, 1893

In 1893, the Bishop Wing (or Bishop Annex) was built alongside the original building, extending toward Punchbowl. Trustee Charles Reed Bishop donated $10,000 toward its construction. Like most of the hospital's buildings, the Bishop Wing was renovated and its floors were used for different purposes many times throughout its history. Bishop was demolished in 1990 to make way for the Queen Emma Tower extension.

The Dawn of a New Century

Disease had one last parting shot before the close of the nineteenth century. On December 12, 1899, a Chinese bookkeeper for a business on Nu'uanu Avenue died of bubonic plague. By the end of the month, there were nine more cases. As president of the Board of Health during the outbreak, Dr. C. B. Wood was determined to prevent an epidemic. The Board of Health set up a quarantine station in Kaka'ako and used military guards for enforcement.

By this time, Chinatown had recovered from the 1886 fire, but it was filled with rickety, run-down wooden structures. Dense living conditions and horrible sanitation created ideal breeding grounds for the rats whose fleas transmitted the plague and other diseases. The Board of Health disinfected buildings, burned garbage, filled overflowing cesspools, and set forty-one fires. When the next controlled burn commenced on January 20, 1900 on Beretania Street near Nu'uanu Avenue, gusts of wind blew the fire to the old Kaumakapili Church. It leaped from building to building until it reached Honolulu Harbor. The fire burned out of control for seventeen days, destroying some 4,000 homes. Although thirty-eight acres had burned, the Board of Health felt a need to set thirty-one additional fires. Honolulu was declared plague-free four months later.

At the end of the nineteenth century, medicine was about to enter the modern era of empirical evidence and scientific discovery that would begin to defeat many previously intractable diseases. The Queen's Hospital was also poised to enter the modern age of medicine.

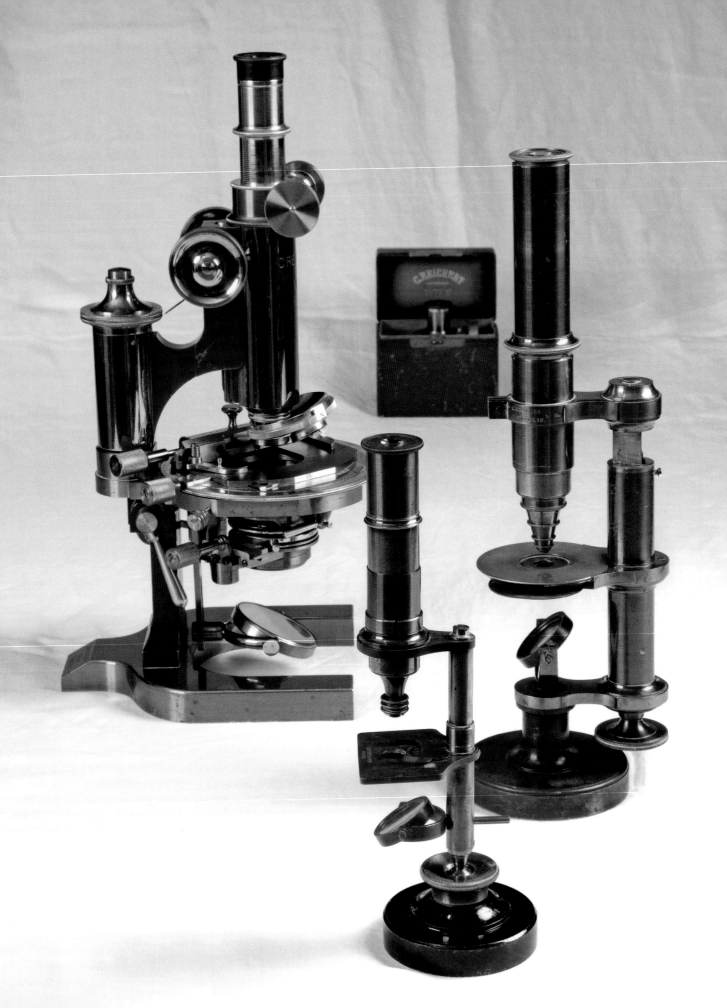

THE MODERN AGE OF MEDICINE

1900–1950

QUEEN'S HOSPITAL
HONOLULU, T. H.   June 13, 1916.
P. O. BOX 614

Hospital stationery.

opposite
Clockwise from left: C. Reichert, Vienna, microscope, no. 16311, purchased in Honolulu in 1904 by Dr. I. Katsuki for $340 ($8,482.39 in 2008 dollars); eyepiece (in brown leather case). Bausch & Lomb Optical Co. microscope, Rochester, New York, circa 1865. Bardou & Son microscope, Paris, circa 1860s.

The modern age of medicine began at the turn of the nineteenth century. Louis Pasteur had strongly promoted the germ theory of disease, and in 1879, Robert Koch devised a series of proofs for the theory. By the turn of the century, the germ theory of disease was accepted worldwide, and bacteria had been solidly linked to infectious diseases. Medicine was about to be revolutionized with new diagnostic equipment and drugs that brought patients back from certain death. Hospitals were becoming widely recognized as more than sick houses for people who could not afford private physician care, and pay patients were growing in numbers at The Queen's Hospital. Beginning in 1905, the hospital entered an eighty-year era of expansion as the population of Hawai'i grew and the demand for medical care increased.

By 1903, there was serious overcrowding at the hospital. "The wards are now so full," reported Queen's superintendent Johannes Eckardt, "that from day to day, I do not know what to do, if say a half dozen patients should come in from the plantations near town."[1] Trustee Charles Reed Bishop donated $35,000 toward a new wing. The total cost of the new building was reported to be about $65,000[2] (about $1.31 million in 2008).[3] The rest of the money would come from a special fund reserved for construction. The three-story addition was named the Pauahi Annex, or Wing, in honor of Bishop's wife, the late Bernice Pauahi Bishop, who died in 1884.

The trustees entered into a contractor's bond, which delivered "$26,666.50 in Gold Coin of the United States of America" to partially finance the new building.[4] Fifty years earlier, payments in U.S. gold coin were common because the value of the various paper currencies circulating in Hawai'i was uncertain. In 1855, William Cooper Parke, then Marshal of the Hawaiian Islands, paid for King Kamehameha III's funeral with $28,000 in gold coin by dividing the sum into two wheelbarrows and walking to businesses to settle accounts.[5] Although everyday transactions using gold coin were rare in the continental United States by 1900, the hospital staff was still paid in gold.

The dedication of Pauahi took place with great fanfare on June 24, 1905. The Hawai'i Government Band (soon to be known as the Royal Hawaiian Band) entertained the public from the second story balcony, which was decorated with "the flags of all nations." Hospital staff gave tours and regaled the guests with coffee, sandwiches, and ice cream.[6] The Pauahi Wing's 18-by-36-foot operating room featured "a tile floor and wainscoting with proper drainage from the center and [was] thoroughly aseptic and capable of being flushed and cleaned over the entire surface." The *Pacific Commercial Advertiser* described it as "white, a dazzling white."[7] The operating room in the old building was kept for emergency and accident cases.

The hospital switched from gas to electricity with the opening of Pauahi. An Otis Electric Elevator was installed, as well as inclines, "thus avoiding the necessity of transportation [of patients] up the stairs." There were three wards

The Pauahi Wing, circa 1905.

opposite
Dr. W. A. Morton of San Francisco gives a surgical clinic demonstrating the first spinal anesthesia in Hawai'i in 1906. The clinic was held in the Pauahi Wing's third floor operating room.

of ten beds each on the ground floor, eight private rooms on the second floor (plus a pantry and dining room), and four private rooms on the third, for a total of forty-two beds. Each floor had the necessary bath and toilet rooms and a portable bathtub that could be transported to any room. Pauahi was built in the same orientation as the original building, although set back about 50 feet. The Bishop Wing intersected the area between the two buildings at a right angle. Now comprising three wings, the hospital formed an inverted *T*, with the main entrance and offices at the center of the head of the *T*. In total, Queen's had 130 beds.[8]

Operating Rooms See the Light

Pauahi's operating room was "well lighted by overhead skylight and northern exposure,"[9] and "compared favorably to those of the best equipped hospitals on the mainland."[10] Surgeons used natural light to operate, so the best operating rooms were built on the top floors of hospitals. Dr. Robert McKibbin Jr. had complained in 1879 that the old operating room had such poor lighting that he was often forced to operate on the open veranda.[11] Even with the advent of electricity, overhead artificial lighting was much less desirable because the surgeon's head would cast a shadow over the operating area. To alleviate this problem for operations at night, one doctor requested "an extension of electric light from the ceiling in the operating room to within a couple of feet of the operating table."[12] As artificial lighting evolved toward the easily maneuverable boom-style lights of today's operating rooms, natural light became less important. The combination of air-conditioning, which allowed windows to remain closed, and modern lighting changed the physical location of operating rooms to in the interior of hospital buildings by the early 1960s.

Aseptic operating rooms like Pauahi's superseded *antiseptic* ones before the turn of the century. Antiseptic surgery in 1867 was achieved by systematically cleaning hands, surgical instruments, wounds, and the surgical theater with a carbolic acid solution, but shortly after, aseptic surgery, which involves steam sterilization and sterile dressings, replaced it. Both antisepsis and asepsis were rare in the United States until the turn of the century, but acceptance was fairly early in Hawai'i.[13]

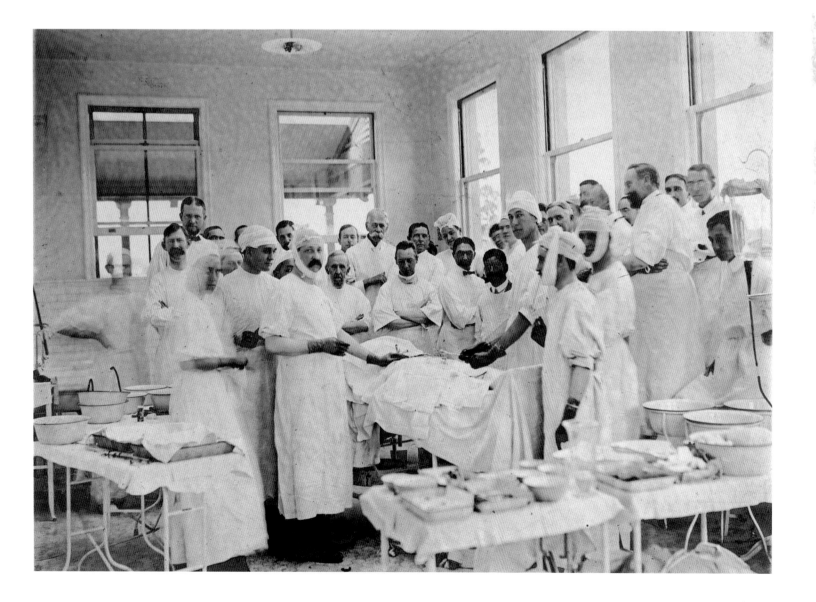

right

Syringe kit, Max Wocher & Son, manufacturers of surgical instruments, 21 & 23 W. 6 St., Cincinnati, Ohio, circa mid to late 1800s.

below

Left: Irrigating syringe, George Tiemann & Co., 107 Park Row, New York, circa 1900. The nickel-plated brass tubular barrel's large oval window is calibrated from one to four ounces. *Center:* Yankauer anesthesia mask with cloth cover, circa 1910. Liquid anesthetics such as ether would be dropped onto the cotton and inhaled by the patient. *Right:* Glass and metal syringe in metal case, circa 1900. The lid reads, "Improved Antitoxin Syringe, H. K. Mulford Company, Philadelphia, Chicago."

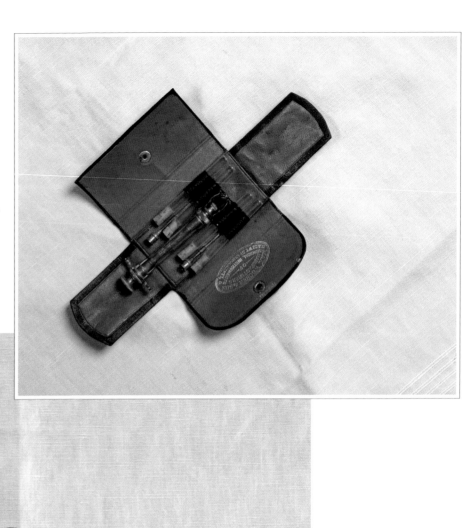

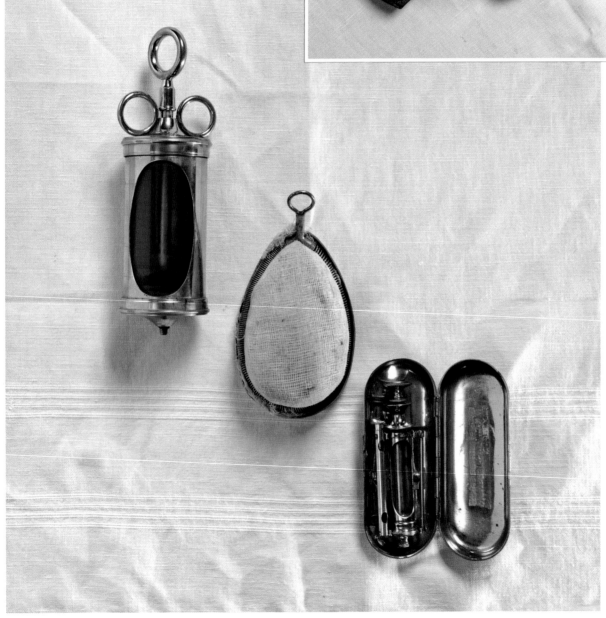

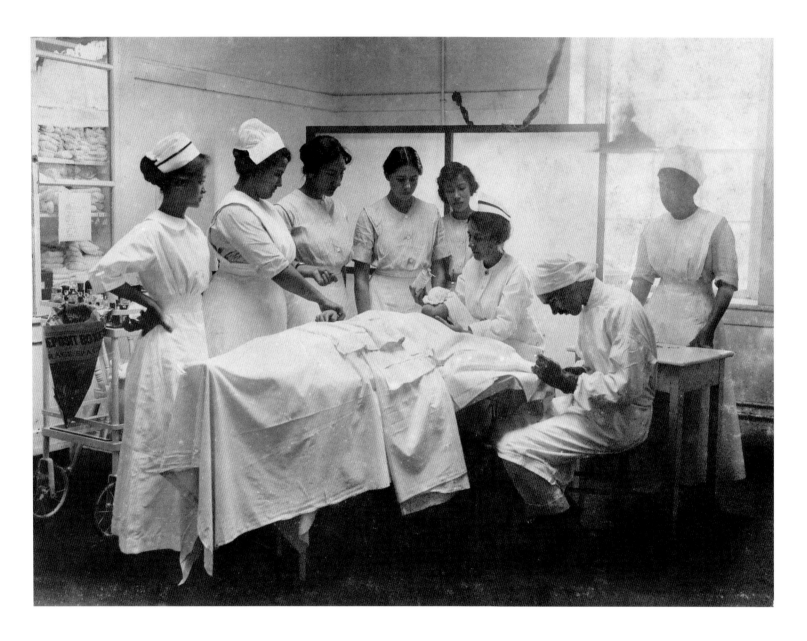

Miss Agnes Collins (seated), superintendent of nurses, administers anesthesia to a patient, while student nurses (without caps) watch, circa 1910s. Miss Lilly Lam, supervisor, monitors the patient's pulse; intern Dr. Joseph Strode is seated on the right.

The Queen's Hospital, circa 1908. *Left to right*: Pauahi Wing,
Bishop Wing, and the original building.

Laura Sax (seated), Queen's head nurse, with two unidentified nurses, 1910.

right
Parke, Davis & Co., hypodermic syringe set, late 1800s. The case includes a glass and metal syringe; two needles; and six tubes of "hyperdermatic tablets" including strychnine nitrate, Apomorphine hydrochl., cocaine hydrochlorate, morphine and atropine, atropine sulphate, and morphine sulphate. The kit was found in Dr. F. L. Miner's Thermo-Cautére case shown on page 35.

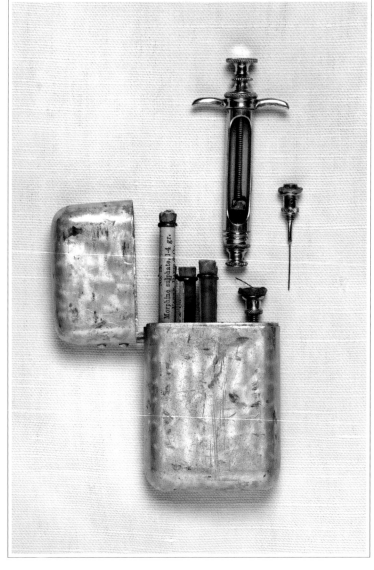

NAME	SEX	NATIONALITY	RESIDENCE		NAME	SEX	NATIONALITY	RESIDENCE	AGE
	M	Japanese	Waianae (Oahu)			M	Japanese	Waianae (Oahu)	

OCCUPATION	SOCIAL CONDITION	ADMITTED	DISCHARGED	RESULT	ATTENDING PHYSICIAN OR SURGEON	OCCUPATION	SOCIAL CONDITION	ADMITTED	DISCHARGED	RESULT	ATTENDING PHYSICIAN OR SURGEON
Plantation-hand	M (?)	Aug. 3, 1904	Sept. 6, 1904	Cured	Waterhouse	Plantation-hand	(?)	Aug. 3, 1904	Sept. 11, 1904	Cured	Wood

P.T.— Cut in stabbing-affray on plantation.
Wds. dressed, primarily, at plantation.
S.P.—

Wds. healed O.K., wds. on hands being last to heal completely

P.T.— Cut in stabbing-affray on plantation.
Wds. dressed, primarily, at Plantation.
S.P.

Queen's patient record book, 1904. The left page describes stab wounds received in a fight at a plantation. If a patient recovered, "cured" was written in the result box.

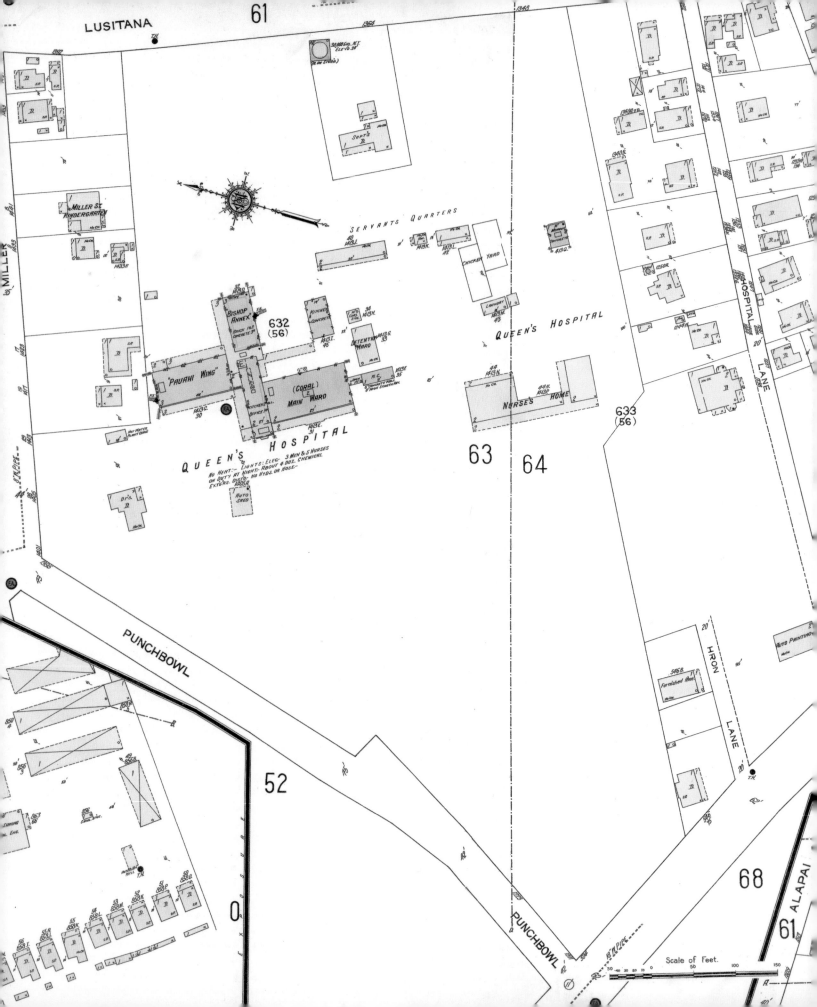

LUSITANA

61

MILLER

Miller St. Kindergarten

Supt's

SERVANTS QUARTERS

BISHOP ANNEX

632
(56)

KITCHEN

DETENTION WARD

CHICKEN YARD

LAUNDRY

Queen's Hospital

"PAUAHI WING"

(CORAL) MAIN WARD

Nurses Home

QUEEN'S HOSPITAL

No Heat: Lights: Elec: 3 Men & 5 Nurses
on Duty at Night: About 4 Doz. Chemical
Extgrs. Dist'd - No Hyds. or Hose:-

633
(56)

63   64

PUNCHBOWL

52

HOSPITAL LANE

HRON LANE

AUTO PRINTING

Furnished Rms

0

PUNCHBOWL

68

ALAPAI

61

Scale of Feet.

Doctors at a picnic on Quarantine Island (now known as Sand Island), 1905.

opposite
Queen's grounds and its structures in 1914. Sanborn Fire Insurance Company Maps of Hawaii, Honolulu, 1914. The hospital provided living quarters for its employees well into the twentieth century. The map shows a long Nurses' Home, servants' quarters, and a doctor's house. To the right of the hospital, a "Hospital Lane" runs parallel to Lauhala Lane (now Street), with many residential dwellings on both sides.

Interns at Queen's

The Queen's Hospital's first intern was Homer Hayes, in 1906. Hayes planned to stay only a short while, but tore up his steamship ticket back to San Francisco after falling in love with the islands. He became a government physician in Honolulu (each district had one), and then on Moloka'i, where he made rounds on horseback. He once had to use a priest's mule, which insisted on stopping at every parishioner's house. To visit patients in Pelekunu Valley on Moloka'i's north coast, he had to swim ashore from a sampan until a ship-to-shore basket tow cable was put into operation. In 1924, Queen's was approved for intern training by the American Medical Association and became the first hospital to attain such standing outside the mainland United States.[14] By 1926, fifty or more practicing physicians in Hawai'i had

received their training at Queen's.[15] A little over thirty years later, 144 doctors in Hawai'i had been trained at the hospital. Today, the Queen Emma Clinics serve as Queen's principal training grounds, with over eighty residents in adult medicine, women's health, and pediatrics.

Public Trouble Leads to Privatization

Despite the new wing and its improvements, trouble had been brewing. Conflicts with the Board of Health over the admission of infectious patients (and to a lesser extent, those considered incurable) and certain indigent patients were heated. The hospital's rules regarding patients with infectious diseases were becoming increasingly strict. By 1907, the list of debarred diseases included "pulmonary tuberculosis, incurable tuberculosis of other organs, cholera, insanity (including delirium tremens), any drug habit of obstreperous & objectionable character, venereal diseases in prostitutes, whooping cough, diphtheria, small pox, leprosy, plague, yellow fever, glanders, alcoholism, maternity cases, chicken pox, measles [and] scarlet fever."[16]

Because the Board of Health had no temporary place to observe suspicious cases except the hallway in front of their offices, some trustees were evidently entertaining the idea of erecting a small ward where these cases could be kept for a few hours. Eckardt advised against the idea, arguing that pay patients would be driven away from the new Pauahi Wing. He further contended that it took days, not hours, to diagnose dangerous diseases like tuberculosis or the plague. An incident in 1905 brought the issue to a head. The Police Patrol brought a man to the hospital. According to Eckardt, the man had "enlarged and painful glands in both groins, both femoral regions, both axillae and on his neck; his temperature was 100 and pulse 100. He also had an eruption resembling Chicken-pox; also Eczema and ulcers on his penis." Unable to get a history, the resident physician denied the man entry. Soon, a dispute arose. Mr. L. E. Pinkham, president of the Board of Health, called the hospital and said that Board of Health doctors had examined the man and "found nothing to warrant his rejection." Later that evening, according to Eckardt, the sheriff called about the case and said, "If you want that $26000.00 appropriation you better take this man in or take the consequences."[17] This was not the first time the Board of Health disagreed with Queen's on admitting a patient.

Eckardt insisted that an observation ward would "greatly

aid the Board of Health and it would RELIEVE [emphasis his] the Hospital of pay-patients.... Also, some doctors will ...advise their patients to go elsewhere. This was true when we admitted Tubercular cases and it will be again true."[18] On October 31, 1905, Pinkham wrote a formal request for an observation ward. The trustees replied that it "would be a menace to the Hospital and would have an injurious effect upon its special sphere of work in the community."[19] A hospital policy was penned: "Refuse no one who needs hospital treatment and is willing to go into the wards, but admit no one suffering from contagious or infectious disease."[20]

Government funds in support of indigent patients appeared to be in jeopardy or had disappeared anyway. In the early days, when most patients were indigent, the hospital was partially funded by the Hawaiian seamen's and passenger's taxes. Both taxes were repealed in 1900 because of changes made to the tax laws when the Territory of Hawaiʻi was organized. The legislature also appropriated money for the hospital. However, the amount from appropriations didn't grow to keep up with inflation, while the amount from pay patients grew dramatically as hospitals became perceived as not just for the poor. For example, in the half year ending December 20, 1873, government appropriations were $6,667, while pay patients brought in only $352.[21] The semiannual report of 1909 showed $6,000 was received from the government and $11,185.45 from pay patients.[22] Queen's also relied on income from endowed beds and the Queen Emma Estate.

Another source of conflict was the admission of certain indigent patients. Even before the Pauahi Wing was built, the Board of Health had begun insisting that Queen's admit patients brought from the plantations. Because Queen's drew on appropriations from the territorial legislature, the Board of Health reasoned that the hospital was obliged to admit indigents of all nationalities, including noncitizens. Eckardt argued that if all such cases were admitted, the hospital would need more wards and additional staff.[23] The issue was related to U.S. equal treatment laws, which prohibited discrimination by race. This was not really a change for Queen's. Although most of the indigents treated in the early days were Hawaiian, indigent "subjects of the Hawaiian Kingdom" of every race were always eligible for free care. However, under the hospital's charter, admissions could be limited by decision of the trustees and the availability of resources.

THE MODERN AGE OF MEDICINE

Endowed Beds

Queen's original charter allowed for the creation of endowed beds. At $5,000 each, an endowed bed provided free care to any patient chosen by the donor or the donor's assignee. If no patient was chosen, the trustees could choose one. In 1891, Trustee C. R. Bishop endowed the first free bed under the control of the Ladies' Strangers' Friend Society. In the same year, Mrs. T. R. Foster endowed a free bed in memory of her late husband, and soon after, Mr. A. A. Corniot of Moloka'i endowed one under the control of the French Consul.

In 1894, the price of endowing a bed was raised to $6,000. Four years later, Mrs. J. F. Hackfeld endowed a bed under the control of the German Benevolent Society, and a year later C. R. Bishop endowed three more under the Ladies' Strangers' Friend Society. The donation amount was incrementally raised to $15,000. The last beds were made possible by the 'I'i heirs in 1927, and by William Henry Baird in 1936 with 244 shares of Waialua Agriculture in lieu of cash. There were sixteen endowed beds in all, and they remained in existence until the cost of caring for patients exceeded the income from the endowments. The money was put into an endowed bed fund, which still helps to pay for indigent care.

opposite
A patient ward on the first floor of the Pauahi Wing, circa 1920s.

The trustees sought legal opinion. A letter from the hospital's attorney stated, "It is our opinion that neither the Board of Health nor any other branch of the Executive department of the Government can legally attach any condition to the receipt of the monies so appropriated which the Legislature has not imposed." He further opined that "the trustees of the Hospital must have a large discretion in the management of the institution, and that they may properly make by-laws or regulations excluding aliens from its benefits."[24]

These irreconcilable differences and financial considerations caused The Queen's Hospital to shed its semipublic character to become a private, nonprofit corporation in 1909. Privatization allowed the hospital to make its own policy decisions as to what was best for its patients and the continued viability of the institution. The trustees expressly stated that "the Hospital was organized for the treatment of cases which are classed as curable. It is not an old person's home, nor a retreat for incurables. [Chronics and incurables were admitted if it was believed that hospital treatment would improve their condition.] It has become a general hospital, but by its charter is permitted to refuse contagious cases."[25] The new charter also reflected a broader purpose. To meet the challenges of a growing population and changing demographics, The Queen's Hospital Corporation would build and operate hospitals for the "treatment of sick and disabled persons, and from time to time enlarge, rebuild and repair such hospitals; and . . . maintain wards and apartments in such hospitals for the treatment of pay persons as well as free wards for the treatment of indigent persons."[26]

Care for Indigent Patients

In 1909, indigent medical care was shifted from the Territory to the county governments—in the case of Queen's, the City and County of Honolulu. By 1955, indigent care costs had risen to $848,461, half of which went to Queen's. After statehood in 1959, the City and County gradually shifted funding to the state and federal governments. In the 1980s, Queen's began to use more and more of its own income to care for the needy. For example, from 1992 to 1996, its expenditure for charity care totaled about $8,334,000, or an average of $1,666,800 per year. In fiscal year 2008–9, Queen's contributed over $45 million in health care services, education, charitable contributions, and uncompensated care to the

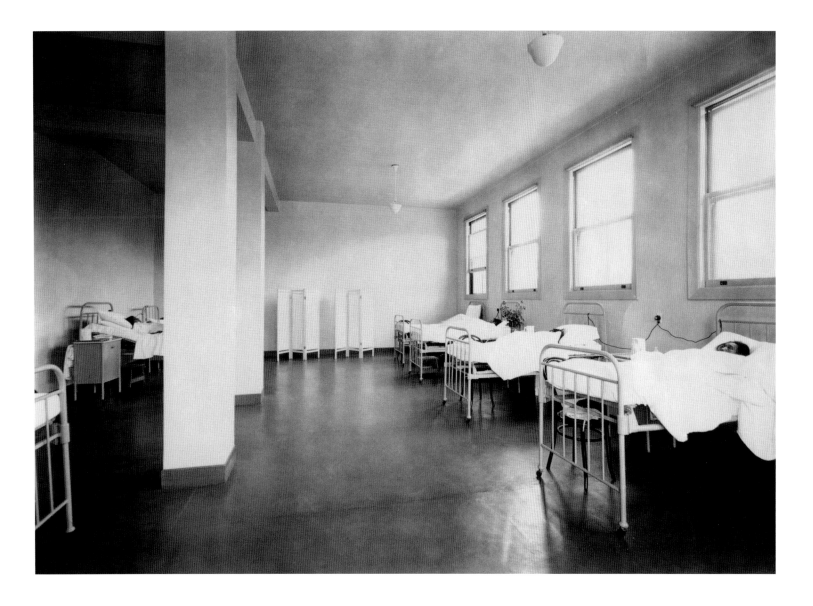

community. Today, patient care is still provided at no charge or at reduced rates for patients who do not have adequate means to pay. Discounts are given based on income and asset thresholds in compliance with state and federal regulations.[27]

Imaging at Queen's

The first medical advancement to allow doctors to peer inside the human body without cutting into it was the invention of the X-ray machine. Discovered by Wilhelm Roentgen in November of 1895 and announced at the start of the new year, the news reached Hawai'i just five weeks later.[28] Later in 1896, the Honolulu Sanitarium became the first institution in Hawai'i to purchase an X-ray machine; Honolulu

hospitals were slower to obtain the technology. The earliest recorded use of an X-ray for diagnostics at The Queen's Hospital is in 1904, for a patient with a fractured leg.[29] The X-ray was apparently obtained elsewhere, as in 1908, the trustees decided to "call the attention of the Executive Committee to the great necessity of a moderne [*sic*] x-ray apparatus,"[30] but did not obtain one until 1910.[31] The first roentgenologist (radiologist) was appointed in 1917.

The X-ray dominated what is now known as "imaging" for many years until the inventions of ultrasound, CT, MRI, and PET scanning. Although still a widely used diagnostic tool, the basic X-ray has limitations, since it does not show soft tissues well and produces two-dimensional images. However, the X-ray opened a window to the possibility of finding other

THE MODERN AGE OF MEDICINE

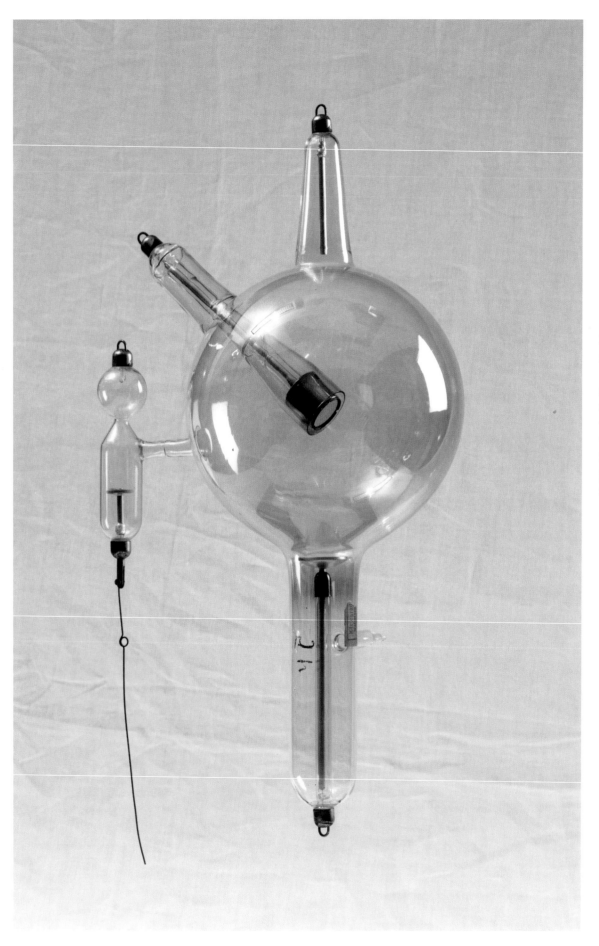

X-ray tube, Müller Rontgenrohre, no. 72203, Germany, circa 1902.

opposite
Sarah Wandell, nuclear medicine technologist, prepares a patient for a PET/CT scan. The monitor in the upper right shows the patient from the opposite end of the scanner.

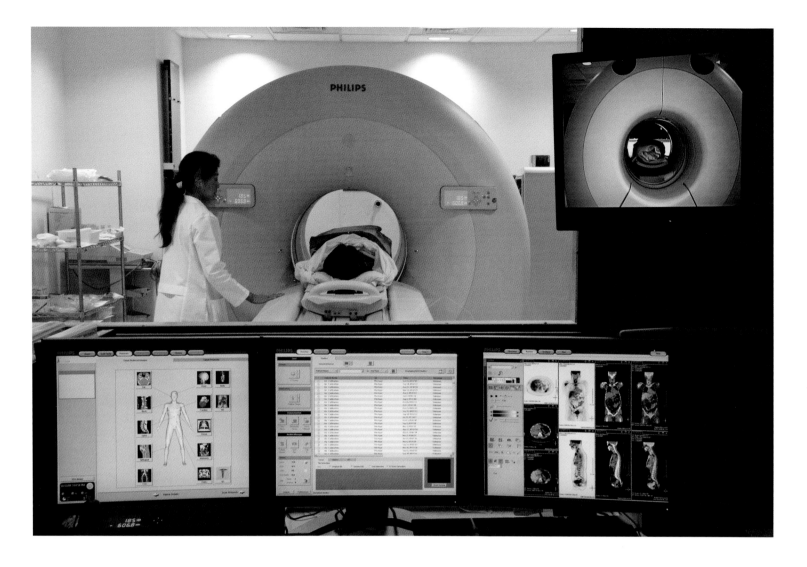

technologies. One was ultrasound, which was adapted from World War I attempts to detect submarines using low-frequency sound waves. The technology became available for medical diagnostics in the 1960s.

Another technology was tomography, which led to computerized axial tomography (CAT or CT for short) scanning. A new use of X-ray technology, tomography produces an image representing a "slice" of tissue. However, a way was needed to build up many of these image slices to have a useful imaging technique. In the 1960s, a device that replaced photographic film with electronic X-ray detectors was invented. Computer technology was later developed to process the massive number of electronic signals needed to create cross-section images, and the CT head scanner became available in 1972. Queen's acquired its first CT head scanner that year, and a whole body scanner in 1973.

Magnetic resonance imaging, or MRI, came into use about ten years later. MRI scanning uses a powerful electromagnet to align the protons of hydrogen atoms in the body. A radio frequency electromagnetic field is then used to briefly alter the alignment of the protons. Different types of tissues give off varying signal lengths, which are computer processed to create detailed, three-dimensional images. MRI has become the principal tool used to diagnose many diseases. CT and MRI scanning have some overlap in function, but each has its advantages, depending on the circumstances. Queen's became the first hospital in Hawai'i to house an MRI system in 1991. From 2007 to 2009, Queen's replaced its MRI and CT scanners with next generation technology, which facilitates the diagnosis of diseases more quickly and with much greater detail. New CT scanners produce images so quickly that radiologists can see the heart in motion, while

THE MODERN AGE OF MEDICINE

software generates three-dimensional images from any view plane. Over 4,500 MRI and 4,000 CT scans are currently performed at Queen's per month.

The late 1980s saw the development of positron emission tomography (PET), in which a radiopharmaceutical "tagged" with glucose is injected into the body. PET scan images show the metabolic activity of cells by the rate glucose is consumed. Cancer can be detected because it consumes glucose at a high rate. Conversely, Alzheimer's disease can be detected in the brain, and the condition of damaged heart muscle is determined by measuring depressed metabolic activity. In 1997, The Queen's Medical Center formed a joint venture called the Hamamastu/Queen's PET Imaging Center to become the first in Hawai'i to offer PET scanning. Because radiopharmaceuticals have a very short half-life, they are manufactured at the Liholiho Cyclotron Building, which was constructed next to the Kamehameha Wing to house a cyclotron. In 2007, Queen's became the first hospital to obtain a PET/CT scanner, which exactly aligns the two types of scans. Now, a tumor's size, shape, mass, and location can be imaged by the CT scanner, while the PET shows where and how rapidly it is growing.

The Ongoing Issues at The Queen's Hospital

Discussions of financial issues offer a window into The Queen's Hospital in the early twentieth century. A report complained that the hospital was being subjected to increasing demands with no corresponding increase in revenue. Expenditures reveal what was expected of the hospital. For example, Queen's had always been responsible for patient burial expenses, including coffins. Now the cost was a burden. "We believe that patients are often brought to the Hospital to die and save the family the burial expense," wrote the secretary of the board of trustees. The secretary cited ten indigent patients, of whom "two died within thirty hours of their admission, one in two days, two in five days, one in nine days and one in twelve days."[32] Emergency cases were treated free of charge. One doctor felt that they should be sent to a physician's office whenever possible; if treated at the hospital, the patient should pay for the dressing, if able, or a charge should be sent to the patient's employer.[33] Some issues have continued to the present. In 1908, nurses were in short supply. Although the hospital gave a service to the public "equal to the best class of mainland hospitals," it was at "considerable disadvantage" because it had to pay steamship passage to bring in nurses. Also, "provisions [food], especially in the line of delicacies, are much more expensive here than on the mainland."[34]

In 1911, there were a total of 130 beds. In addition to the superintendent, the house physician, and two assistant doctors, the staff comprised a superintendent of nurses, fifteen staff nurses, a housekeeper, an office assistant, and hospital attendants, for a total of fifty-one employees. There were 1,272 patients that year and 588 surgeries (appendectomies headed the list at 123);[35] the average length of stay for a patient was twenty days.

Pandemic Disease and War

The Queen's Hospital Training School for Nurses (later called The Queen's Hospital School of Nursing) opened in 1916, just before the U.S. entry into World War I in 1917 and the influenza pandemic of 1918 to 1920. The call to duty in the armed services made it impossible to secure interns and graduate nurses. Resident physician Dr. F. F. Alsup and intern Dr. Joseph Strode were called into the army. Strode's replacement was also called, leaving the hospital without an intern. Even the secretary of the board of trustees, Bruce Cartwright Jr., resigned temporarily because he was called to active duty in the army. The trustees were also forced to deal with anti-German sentiment when the press and others commented on the German parentage of hospital employees.

The first cases of influenza on O'ahu hit military bases at the end of June 1918.[36] Soon, there were over a thousand cases. A victory parade in downtown Honolulu on November 11, 1918 marked the end of World War I, but cases of the flu continued to mount. Like the measles outbreak in 1861, an exception was made for the admission of flu patients. Toward the end of the war, a building (vacated by a public kindergarten) near Miller Street, later named Kalanimoku, was used as a twenty-five-bed isolation unit. By January of 1919, The Queen's Hospital was inundated with influenza patients.[37] Physicians, nurses, and hospital beds were in short supply, and the lanai of the original building was full of patients.[38] When it was over, the pandemic had claimed an estimated 21 million lives worldwide, including 675,000 Americans and over 2,300 people in Hawai'i.[39]

The Turning Tide against Infectious Diseases

By the 1920s, diphtheria was being brought under control. This deadly childhood disease released a powerful toxin that could kill a child by causing inflammation of the heart and nervous system even if death did not occur from suffocation caused by swelling of the windpipe. An antitoxin developed in the 1890s led to the discovery of one for tetanus, which then led to the discovery of toxoids that produced long-term immunity from diphtheria. An immunization campaign in Hawaiʻi in 1929 cut deaths from diphtheria in half within a year. In 1936, a law was passed requiring diphtheria vaccination for children entering school.

The stigma against most infectious diseases was beginning to fade. With advances in hygiene and infection control, it was now believed safe to treat typhoid patients at The Queen's Hospital, and cases were steadily decreasing. In 1926, Dr. Joseph Strode declared victory:

Queen's nurses participate in a World War I Armistice Day parade in downtown Honolulu on November 11, 1918.

The eradication of typhoid fever by immunization and methods of sanitation is probably the greatest achievement of preventive medicine. Thousands of soldiers died of typhoid in the Spanish-American War, many more than from the casualties of war. During World War I the incidence of typhoid in the U.S. Army was practically nil.[40]

Alice Yoshida, a Honolulu resident, recalls that her brother was hospitalized at Queen's in the 1920s for typhoid fever, but remembers no particular fear of infectious diseases. However, without antibiotics, infection was still a dire threat. In the same year Yoshida's brother was at Queen's, her grandfather's foot became infected. With no way to control the spreading infection, a Queen's doctor urged amputation.

THE MODERN AGE OF MEDICINE

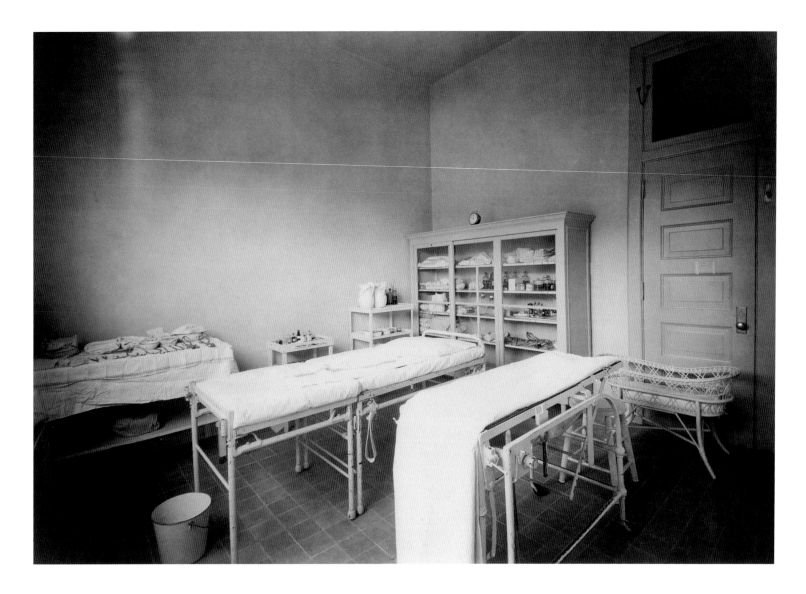

Yoshida's grandfather understandably hesitated, but when he later gave his consent, it was too late. He died of sepsis before the end of the year.[41]

Robert Faus (1897–1983) and Marie Faus (1896–1975)
While Robert Faus was a psychiatric intern at Cook County Hospital in Chicago, he saw a notice that read, "Interns and Residents Wanted in Honolulu," signed by a Dr. Paul Withington. He sent a Western Union telegram to Withington and two days later received $250 for the trip to The Queen's Hospital in Honolulu. He quickly sent another telegram to Miss Marie Keim, a former classmate at Colorado Medical School, and asked, "Will you marry me and go to Honolulu?"[42] The couple married in Colorado and arrived at Queen's in July 1921.

The memoirs of Dr. Marie Faus, Queen's first female intern, give a flavor of the hospital in the 1920s when she arrived with her husband, who was also an intern.[43] The two doctors became known affectionately as Dr. Marie and Dr. Bob. "There was no such thing as a recovery room near the operating section," wrote Dr. Marie. The operating room was on the third floor of the Pauahi Wing at the time. After surgery, patients were wheeled "down the open porches used as a corridor" to their unscreened ward (mosquito nets were still used), where a nurse had a bed prepared for them. "Oxygen was delivered by the wind," she wrote. "If now and then a dash of rain came…towels were handy. It was enough to give a mainland-trained surgeon a nervous breakdown, but it worried no one here. That was the way it was done at Queen's."

Although the residents of Honolulu would have probably

said that the city had grown, Dr. Marie wrote that taro still grew in all of Moʻiliʻili, and Waikīkī was a swamp full of duck ponds. In addition to her work in pediatrics at Queen's, she was also appointed as Kapiʻolani Maternity Hospital's first intern. Dr. Marie rode the streetcar there whenever called to deliver a baby. After completing her internship at Queen's in 1922, Dr. Marie went into private practice with Dr. Withington, who taught her never to let a patient leave empty handed, even if it meant giving them harmless samples.

opposite

A Queen's operating room, circa 1930s.

The Pauahi Wing's nursery, 1926.

"Patients were often put to bed on the lanais or porches," wrote Dr. Marie, who specialized in maternity and pediatrics at Queen's, "and my delivery room at the end of the second story had a large, red Poinciana tree so close one could lean out and pick the flaming blossoms. I delivered many a baby in that tree." It seems inconceivable that patients could be left on the lanai, but photographs of the period show that awnings and curtains were put on the original building, and sections of lanai were almost completely enclosed with glass-paned windows. At the turn of the century, hospitals were not thought of as places for women to give birth, but by the 1920s, when Dr. Marie arrived, Queen's was bringing birthing to the hygienic hands of hospital professionals rather than midwives. Dr. Marie was later one of the organizers of free child health clinics at Palama Settlement. She also

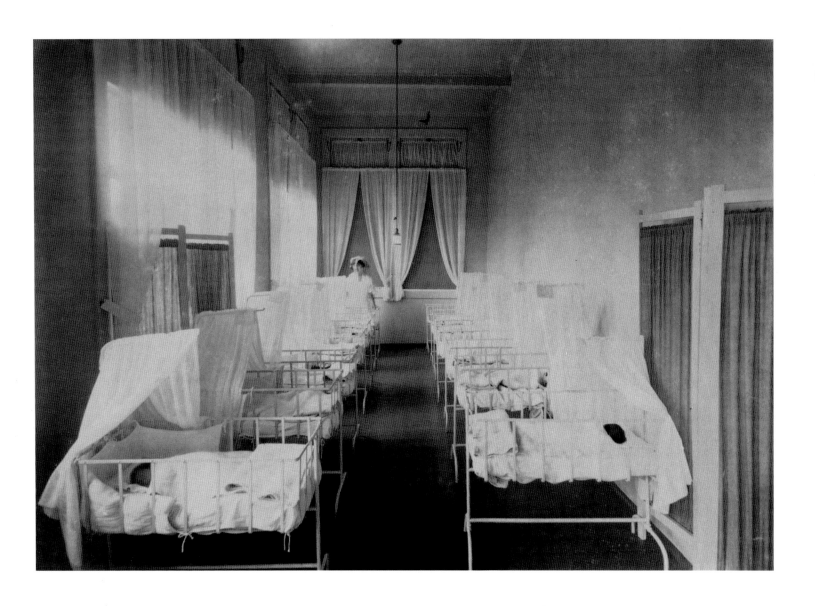

founded the Bureau of Maternal and Child Health and was resident physician at the Hawai'i State Hospital.

Dr. Bob also went into private practice after completing his internship. He and Dr. Marie were asked by Governor Farrington to conduct a survey of the O'ahu Insane Asylum in 1923. Detailing the dreadful conditions they observed, the Fauses' report was instrumental in a legislative appropriation of $75,000 for the purchase of land in Kāne'ohe for a new hospital, which today is the Hawai'i State Hospital. Dr. Bob also served as police surgeon from 1925 to 1930. A pioneer in blood transfusions, he started a mobile blood bank. While he was a city and county physician, Dr. Bob helped establish the City and County Emergency Unit (Maluhia) at Queen's. Dr. Bob was posthumously awarded the Bronze Star for outstanding work in establishing civilian aid stations and ambulance service after the December 7, 1941 attack on Pearl Harbor. He was on his way to give a lecture on the importance of emergency preparedness when the attack came. Instead, he spent the next three days supervising the treatment of wounded civilians from the armory near 'Iolani Palace.

When Drs. Bob and Marie first arrived at Queen's, they stayed in a room in the nurses' quarters. "Then Miss Mullen, the head nurse who was a spinster, discovered to her horror that I was living with my husband in the Hospital," related Dr. Marie. "She went to the superintendent, an elderly man, and they apparently let their imaginations get the best of them about that bed in the nurses' quarters. I was . . . told this would never do with those innocent girls in the same building." Dr. Marie delivered a saucy comeback: "Why was it so astonishing? The nurses must have lived at home where their parents were married, or at least I hope they were married, and occupied the same room!" Nevertheless, Drs. Bob and Marie took an apartment on Vineyard Street.

Living at Queen's

From the time it was built and well into the twentieth century, The Queen's Hospital customarily provided living quarters for its employees. Dr. C. B. Wood recalled that in 1892, the purveyor, Johannes Eckardt, lived with his family in a cottage on the premises. In 1897, Eckardt drew the trustees' attention to the fact that nurses were living in four of eight private rooms in the Bishop Annex, and so a Nurses' Home was completed in October 1898. Details on the interns'

Nurses on the grounds of Queen's, 1910. *Opposite:* The 1898 Nurses' Home in the foreground, with the Queen Emma Building (later renamed Nalani) in the background, circa 1920s.

cottage and other residences that once existed on the premises are scarce, but references to them in trustee correspondence are numerous. The 1914 Sanborn Fire Insurance Map (p. 54) shows a sizable Nurses' Home, superintendent's home, and a doctor's house. About 500 feet to the right of the main building, a "Hospital Lane" ran parallel to Lauhala Lane (now Street) with many residential dwellings on both sides.

If there was no room at Queen's, the hospital would provide an allowance for room rent. In 1919, nurses brought in from the mainland were temporarily housed at the Young Hotel until the superintendent "was able to secure two apartments at the New Engleside on Vineyard Street near the grounds," where he put five of them.[44] Construction of new living quarters was fairly frequent. A new wing was built onto the Nurses' Home in 1922. In 1925, the trustees approved "that a cottage be erected for the seamstress; [and] that a sleeping porch be added to the cottage of Miss Jackson, Superintendent of the Training School."[45]

A 1944 map (p. 77) shows how completely the configuration of buildings changed in thirty years. Hospital Lane no longer exists; instead, there is a series of six elongated buildings labeled "employee dormitories" surrounding a large courtyard along Lusitana Street. Nurses' and female house staff quarters were located about thirty yards from male quarters near the corner of Miller and Lusitana streets. Space was probably the biggest factor in changing the tradition of live-in employees. In 1911, Queen's had just fifty-one employees; by 1959, there were 671 (currently, there are about 3,700). Maps show that an ever-growing hospital rapidly occupied the areas where employees once lived.

Living at Queen's created a close camaraderie, however. Everyone knew everyone else. Ethel Matsui, a 1956 graduate of the School of Nursing, remembers playing softball with the residents in front of the Harkness Nurses' Home. "The residents and student nurses used to put on a May Day

program on the front lawn with a king and queen, a decorated stage and ethnic dances," Matsui remembers. "The staff and patients came to watch."[46] On Sundays, the Royal Hawaiian Band played for the patients in front of the lobby, and the nursing students would stand on the second floor balcony of the Nalani Wing to listen. Students lived on campus until the School of Nursing closed in 1968. Interns were the last to leave in the 1970s.

Dr. Nils Paul Larsen (1890–1964)

In 1922, hospital trustees appointed Dr. Nils Paul Larson as pathologist. Although not the hospital's first pathologist, Larsen established the Pathological Laboratory with a full-time technician. After becoming the hospital's first medical director the following year, Larsen would not only define the direction of the hospital for the next twenty years but also would greatly influence plantation medicine and the health of the people of Hawai'i.

Born in Stockholm, Sweden, Nils Larsen came to the United States with his parents when he was three. After graduating from Cornell University Medical College, he went to New York Hospital, where he was a special research intern and assistant pathologist. World War I interrupted his work in 1917, and Dr. Larsen entered the U.S. Army Medical Corps and went overseas with the 106th Infantry in 1918. During the war, he rescued a wounded soldier trapped on the front lines, then went back to search the shell holes until all the wounded and killed of his regiment had been found. Larsen was awarded the Silver Star for gallantry, and he held the rank of major when he left the service in 1919.

After the war, Larsen became an instructor in bacteriology at Cornell, served as a visiting physician at various hospitals, and published research on pneumonia and asthma. After his marriage to Sara Elizabeth Lucas (who Larsen first met while visiting his brother in Hawai'i), he accepted his appointment as pathologist at Queen's. At the hospital, he also established the Occupational Therapy Department in 1929, organized the Research Department, and helped with the development of The Queen's Hospital Training School for Nurses. Larsen instituted a lively, weekly clinic, which left many a doctor feeling bruised; but forty to fifty doctors showed up anyway every Thursday morning. The president of the board of trustees, E. F. Bishop, remarked, "The professional atmosphere of the Hospital, as well as the esprit de corps, has greatly improved during the year past through the conscientious effort and high ambition of Dr. N. P. Larsen to make the institution headquarters for clinical discussion and research by the medical profession of the community."[47]

Jetter & Scheerer pocket surgical set, Tuttlingen, Germany, 1900–50. The set consists of thirteen chrome-plated surgical instruments. The hypodermic needle is marked "YALE-LUER—B.D. & CO."

opposite

Dr. Frank J. Putnam's physician's kit, unknown manufacturer, 1926. Contents include: urotropin; barbital; salicylic acid; bromide; calomel; iron, arsenic, and strychnine; cascara sagrada; pepsin; aloin, belladonna, strychnine, and cascara; phenacetin salol; castor oil; alcohol; adrenaline ampules; camphor; sodium; codeine; amytal; phenacetine and salol; strychnine; racebo; opium and lead acetate; corrective for infants; and aspirin.

Plantation Medicine

In the early plantation days, medical attention was scarce, although a doctor was available if needed. Births took place in the two-room houses where workers lived, and a husband was more likely than a doctor to deliver a baby. By 1900, most plantations had Western-trained doctors. After completing his internship at The Queen's Hospital in 1909, Dr. L. L. Sexton recounted his experiences as a plantation doctor in Hilo:

Transportation was by horse and buggy over muddy, frequently impassable roads. The saddlebag filled with my total armamentarium was always ready in the buggy so that I could mount a mule for a trip into the foothills to see what? —a delivery, ruptured appendix, strangulated hernia, extraction of an aching tooth. Operation a must. How? Easy. A five gallon oil can, build a fire; instruments sterilized, local preparation—soap and water—old rags soaked in strong Lysol as drapes. Anesthetic—chloroform, easy to carry. Anesthetist—mama-san, trained on the spot with hand signals. Not my skill but the grace of God."[48]

A sugar plantation in leeward O'ahu depicted by Shirley Russell, 1929. After a day's work, plantation workers return home through miles of fields.

By 1910, a hospital with a full nursing staff was established on the Hamakua Coast of the island of Hawai'i to serve three plantations. Before they began to decline in the 1950s, there were twenty-seven self-contained plantations with medical facilities, housing, schools, stores, and community centers. At one time, laborers numbered about 53,000; their dependents swelled the number to 103,000.[49]

Plantation hospitals were at their peak in the 1930s. Every plantation either had its own hospital or shared one with a neighboring plantation. Many plantation doctors, who numbered forty-eight by the end of World War II, trained at The Queen's Hospital, and a majority of nurses came from The Queen's Hospital School of Nursing. By 1949, mortality on the plantations was the lowest of all rural areas across the United States, and tuberculosis was lower than average. Most plantation hospitals met national standards, and there was a better distribution of doctors and hospitals than in any other state or territory.[50]

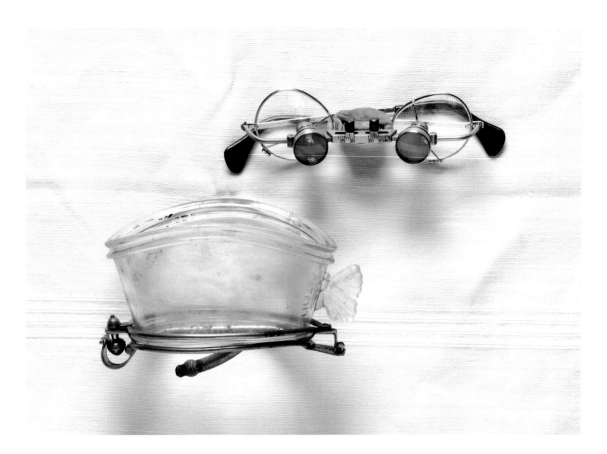

American Optical magnifying spectacles with 2x Carl Zeiss Jena lenses and 12-K gold-filled frame, 1930s.

Glass anesthesia mask, early to mid twentieth century. The anesthesia was administered via a tube, an improvement over the earlier drop mask (see page 48).

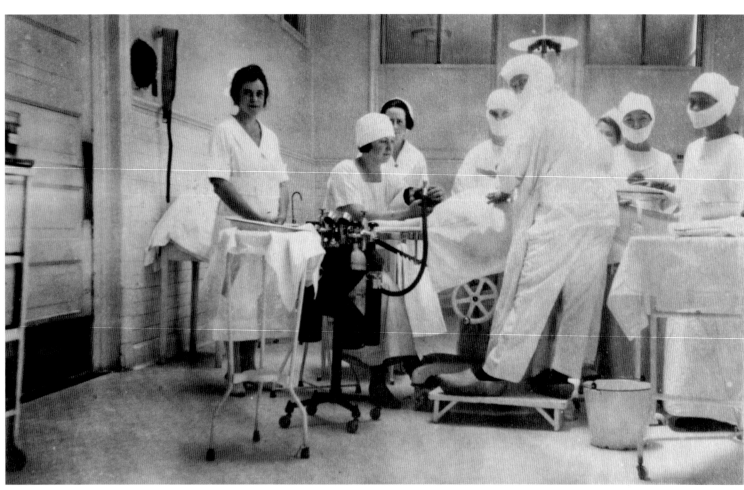

Larsen found other ways to better the health of the community, such as fighting to improve Hawai'i's milk supply, an initiative that led to a large drop in infant mortality.

It would be difficult to overestimate the influence and leadership of Dr. Larsen on plantation medicine in Hawai'i.[51] Larsen concerned himself with the maternal health and child care of immigrant laborers on O'ahu plantations. He established the Ewa Plantation Health Project, which put a well-baby clinic in four of the Ewa plantation camps. At the clinics, he and Martha Jones, a research associate at Queen's and the director of the project, supervised the feeding of balanced diets to babies and gave instructions on care to mothers. Larsen promoted birth control and birth spacing to reduce the mortality rate of mothers and babies due to too-frequent pregnancies. Many elementary school children's teeth were rotted to stumps. The clinics corrected this in one generation with an emphasis on diet. When he became medical advisor to the Hawai'i Sugar Planters' Association (HSPA) in 1930, Larsen developed a medical and health education program that helped the plantations achieve the lowest disease and mortality rates among American industries. In a speech to the HSPA, Larson made a passionate plea: "At your experiment station, scientists have demonstrated that it pays to improve the crops. Let me show that it also pays to improve human beings."[52]

As the consultant for the bulletin *Plantation Health*, Larsen disseminated information to doctors on how to solve health problems. Under his leadership, The Queen's Hospital Research Department collaborated with the Board of Health to supply formula for infants and supplements for children. He worked to improve the health of plantation workers by studying the foods they ate and adding supplements to their diet, which consisted mostly of white rice. To balance this diet, Larsen convinced plantation stores to sell food at cost

opposite
Dr. George F. Straub performs surgery wearing wooden Dutch shoes, circa 1920s.

and promoted the planting of fruit trees in the yards of employees. Larsen held the position of HSPA medical advisor for over thirty years.

A multitalented individual who was known for his etchings and color photographs, Larsen wrote and directed historical pageants for Queen's and the Hawai'i Medical Society. He also wrote many articles on the history of The Queen's Hospital, and began collecting the historical material that led to the creation of the Queen's Historical Room.

Two hours before his death in 1964, Dr. Nils Larsen sat reading a magazine and holding an oxygen mask over his face while waiting for the results of his EKG. He had just finished writing a note to Dr. Paul White in Boston describing his symptoms, believing that it might be of value in the study of heart disease.[53] So great was his presence in plantation medicine that a writer later commented that the idealism and leadership he brought seemed to have died with him.[54]

The Modern Age of Hospitals

By 1920, overcrowding was a persistent problem at Queen's. There was always a waiting list, and the overflow from the wards spilled out onto the verandas. Planning for the largest building project in The Queen's Hospital's history began in 1921. For the first time since King Kamehameha IV and Queen Emma appealed to the people of Hawai'i for building funds, the public was asked to subscribe, eventually coming through with $500,000. The ambitious expansion project called for the construction of two new major wings: the Queen Emma Building (later called Nalani) and the Liholiho Wing. The cost of the Queen Emma Building was estimated at $438,500 (about $4.3 million in 2008 dollars),[55] and a substantial temporary building would have to be built behind Bishop. The Liholiho Wing would be built concurrently with the Queen Emma Building. The Nurses' Home also needed an eight-room addition, and the Pauahi and Bishop wings required $52,000 in repairs and renovations.[56]

In 1922, the trustees authorized the contractor Charles Ingvorsen to "remove the old coral Hospital Building and as much of the old brick building adjoining same [the new building would cut into Bishop] as is necessary to make space for the new Hospital Building."[57] Expenses of the removal were covered by the salvage from the old building, except for the cornerstone, which was kept by the hospital.[58]

The cost of the three-story Queen Emma Building was reduced by using less expensive materials and postponing some refinements. The trustees substituted wood window frames for metal, an oak counter for marble, and cement front steps for brick. Omissions included window shades, awnings, elevators, and a porte cochere. Instead, the old elevator was put in good working order. Plumbing for the third floor was roughed in, and the roof was temporary. In spite of the compromises, architect Charles W. Dickey created the classic Queen's façade that characterized the hospital through the middle of the twentieth century.

C. W. Dickey designed hundreds of buildings and residences in Hawai'i, many of which are on the National Register of Historic Places. Early in his career, Dickey felt

the California Mission style was appropriate for Hawai'i. His pre- to early-1900s buildings include Pauahi Hall at Punahou School and the Stangenwald Building in downtown Honolulu. As his work matured leading up to the 1920s, Dickey modified his style, stating that "Hawaiian architecture is distinctive to itself," and adapted other styles to "fit local conditions." After designing the Queen Emma Building and the Liholiho Wing for Queen's, he went on to design the Alexander and Baldwin Building (1926) and the U.S. Immigration Office (1931) in downtown Honolulu. Later, he designed the Harkness Nurses' Home (1932) and the Mabel Smyth Memorial Building (1941) at Queen's. Inspired by Hawaiian grass houses, Dickey's architecture is characterized by low-lying, cream-colored stucco walls and graceful, sloping roofs of variegated green and russet tiles. His trademark roof became known as the "Dickey" or "Hawaiian" roof.[59]

The Liholiho Wing, named after Alexander Liholiho, was built behind the right side of the Queen Emma Building and perpendicular to it, extending back toward Punchbowl. Three wings—Liholiho, the Queen Emma Building, and Bishop—now formed a *U* shape with a courtyard in the middle. (The fourth wing, Pauahi, remained to the left.) The first floor of the Queen Emma Building housed four ten-bed wards for male medical and surgical patients. The second floor had twenty-one private rooms, each with a private bath and lanai.

opposite

The Queen Emma Building (Nalani), circa 1925, showing the ornate crest above the entrance and third floor awning.

Although most of the old façade has been replaced, the crest as it appears today is shown at right. Below, Queen's interns and residents at the entrance of the building, circa 1927.

The third floor was left unfinished due to lack of funds, and was used for offices and outpatients; obstetrical patients were placed there after the floor was finished.

The Queen Emma Building was partially occupied in 1924, and together with Liholiho, had a formal public opening on May 12, 1925 on National Hospital Day, which commemorates Florence Nightingale's birth. The new lobby housed telecommunications, which consisted of a switchboard and two operators. The Emergency Unit was located at the far right end of the building's first floor. The Queen Emma Building was later renamed "Nalani," a nickname for Emma Kaleleonalani, but it continued to be called by its original name at least until 1941. The building's ornate crest with the letters "QH" can still be seen above the third floor windows today. A fourth floor was later added to both Nalani and Liholiho. In 1949, a coffee shop with a soda fountain and service counter was opened in Nalani. Until the 1970s, the arched windows of the third floor below the crest were open-air balconies. Nalani is no longer as wide and grand as it once was. The construction of the 'Iolani Wing in 1960 and

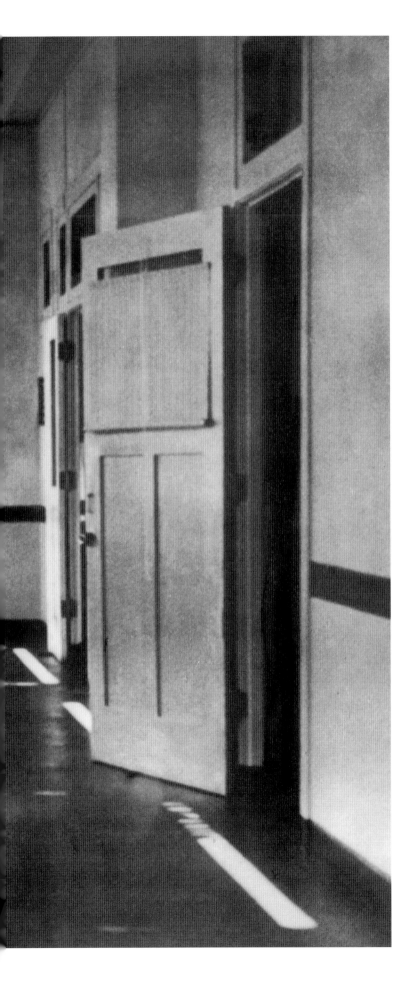

Patients rest in front of the open-air windows on the lanai of the Queen Emma Building, circa 1930.

the new Pauahi Wing in 1966, both of which flank Nalani, clipped the building on either side, and a new lobby was built in front of it, replacing the first floor façade.

The Liholiho Wing was finally completed in 1937, at which time the building was extended 34 feet. Queen's historian Margery Hastert remembered these "old days" when patients stayed much longer, and because of that, became friends. The halls of the hospital would resound with music—patients often brought out their ukulele and began singing.[60] In 1943, staffer Grace Hunter wrote in the *Queen's Messenger* (an employee newsletter) that each of the five wards on Liholiho 1 had its own character. The eye, ear, nose, and throat ward was the first to be gotten in order in the morning, after which "a great somnolence descends and all is quiet except for the soothing presence of its presiding spirit going quietly about her work." In contrast, the fracture ward bustled with activity "accentuated by the hum of radios, the conversation of men and the swish of busy nurses as they valiantly strive, amid pulleys, ropes and casts, to create order and comfort among their charges." Hunter called the next ward, which housed minor surgical cases, "the men's club," since most of the patients were able to walk around and many a good card game could be found, accompanied by "loud remarks, laughter and homely witticisms." Another ward had a more serious tone, with big abdominal cases, head fractures, and spinal operations. "Here a competent but slightly harassed nurse may be seen diligently copying orders from Dr. [Ralph] Cloward's little white book." The last ward on the end, for major accident and critical illness cases, was the most serious of all, wrote Hunter. Silence reigned.[61]

Liholiho 1's floor plan would surprise those whose experience is only with the modern hospital. There was no central corridor running lengthwise through the floor (although the upper floors had them). Entry to the wards was via the lanai. The nurses' station, a small separate structure on the

Patient rooms open onto a cloistered walkway on Liholiho 1, 1927.

courtyard side connected by a roofed walkway, housed a medicine room and a bathroom, but only had three walls, with the open side facing Liholiho. Leatrice Nakashima, RN, began her nursing career in 1970 at Queen's and recounted her experiences on Liholiho 1, which had remained largely unchanged.[62] The outside doors to the wards were always open, she recalls. There were no screens, but Nakashima supposes that the healthy breeze blew the mosquitoes away. The doors were only shut during heavy rain, which would turn the Liholiho 1 lanai into a stream. The maintenance crew would line the walkway with sandbags—not to block the water, but for the nurses to walk on. To avoid wet shoes and stockings, some nurses would go barefoot until the nursing supervisor asked sternly, "Don't we have a dress code?"

Nakashima, who worked the night shift, said that the wards were completely dark during sleeping hours; in those days, beds did not have individual lights. To check patients' vitals signs and Foley bags, nurses used a portable lamp or flashlight to peer behind the ceiling-hung curtains that provided privacy. When she was new to the unit, she didn't know about the long-term patient who liked cats. The patient would surreptitiously save food to lure stray cats to her bed. When Nakashima reached the patient's bed and shined her flashlight in, she screamed: three pairs of glowing green eyes shown back at her.

In the 1920s, The Queen's Hospital began focusing on the infrastructure necessary to support growing medical needs, technology, and added personnel. The trend in medicine was increased specialization. By 1924, in addition to two general physicians and two surgeons, there were specialists

The Queen's Hospital, circa 1945.

1 Nalani Wing 1924
2 Bishop Wing1893
3 Pauahi Wing 1905
4 Liholiho Wing 1925
5 Kina'u Wing 1945
6 Maluhia 1930
7 Harkness Nurses' Home 1932
8 Nurses' Dining Room
9 Pool
10 Mabel Smyth Building 1941
11 Blood Bank 1941
12 Hale Kula 1943
13 Employee Cottages
14 Employee Dormitories

below
The Pauahi Wing with a
new façade, circa 1925.

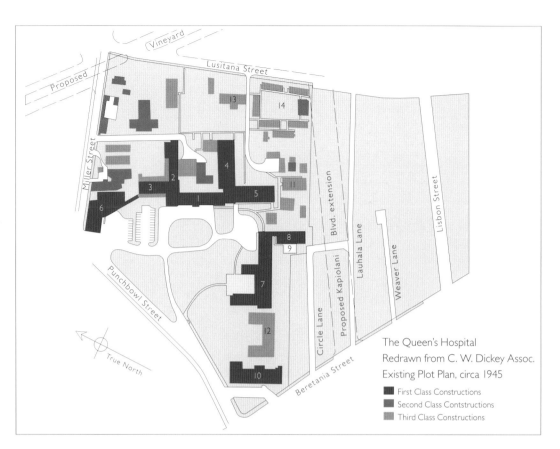

The Queen's Hospital
Redrawn from C. W. Dickey Assoc.
Existing Plot Plan, circa 1945

■ First Class Constructions
■ Second Class Contstructions
■ Third Class Constructions

Queen's laboratory, 1925.

opposite
Surgical suite corridor and operating room, circa 1924.

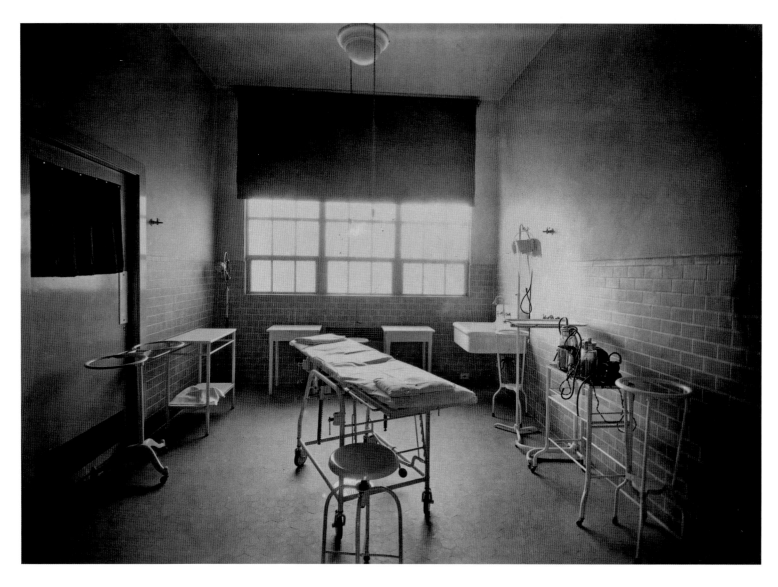

The Queen Emma Building
(Nalani) lobby, circa 1936.

right
Queen Emma Building, 1939.

A student nurse changes a patient's surgical dressing, circa 1930s.

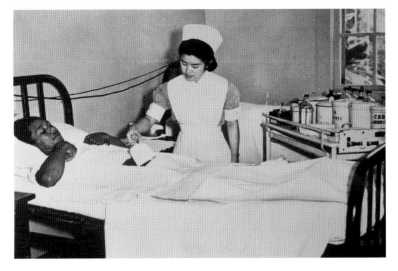

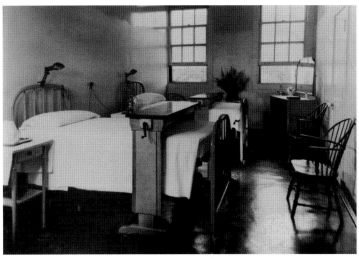

above
A room in the Queen Emma Building (Nalani), circa 1930s.

below
A Liholiho 3 private room for the well-to-do, circa 1938.

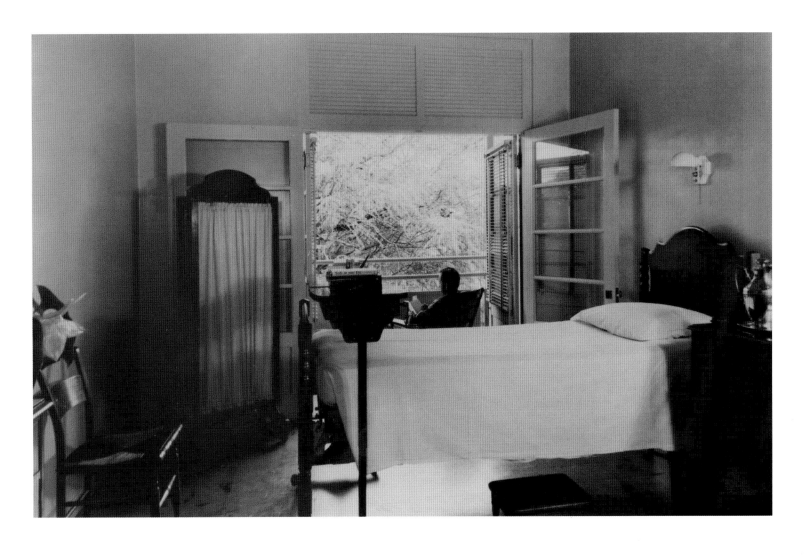

for eye, ear, nose, and throat; genito-urinary diseases; dermatology; obstetrics; physio and mechano therapy; and psychiatry. A pathologist and roentgenologist (radiologist) had been appointed earlier. The next year, gynecology was added, followed by a dental surgeon in 1926.[63]

Rehabilitation Therapies

Occupational therapy and physio-therapy (now called physical therapy) got their start at The Queen's Hospital in the 1920s. A speech defect clinic (now called speech-language pathology) began in 1931. These therapies are now under rehabilitation services at Queen's.

Established in 1929, the occupational therapy (OT) department resulted from the vision of Dr. Nils Larsen and the volunteer work of Mrs. Laura N. Dowsett, who served as director until 1945. Patients were taught crafts such as *lauhala* weaving, soap carving, patchwork, crocheting, basketry, and coconut carving, among others. When an elephant was accidentally shot at the Honolulu Zoo, the hospital's OT department somehow procured the tusks, which amounted to twenty-three pounds of ivory. A patient, who had honed his craft on bones from the kitchen, sawed the tusks into thin disks and etched pictures on them with dental tools.[64] Patient crafts were sold to help finance the work of the department. In the days of lengthy convalescence, many patients found a new purpose through crafts. "Give a patient a nice interesting piece of work and will power does the driving, brings contentment as well as physical restoration," said Mrs. Dowsett.[65]

Although enthusiastically promoted by some, occupational therapy was slow to be accepted by doctors, who thought the therapists "were just a group of society women,

previous page
The Queen's Hospital front lawn landscaped with royal palms, circa 1941.

this page and opposite page, from top
Various therapeutic activities in the 1930s and 1940s at Queen's included Hawaiian *lauhala* weaving, operation of a manually powered scroll saw, and reading in the Occupational Therapy "Library Corner." *Opposite:* Mrs. Laura Dowsett, head of Occupational Therapy, helps a patient with *lauhala* weaving. Polio treatments included an iron lung (circa 1950s), and a paralysis pool (1941).

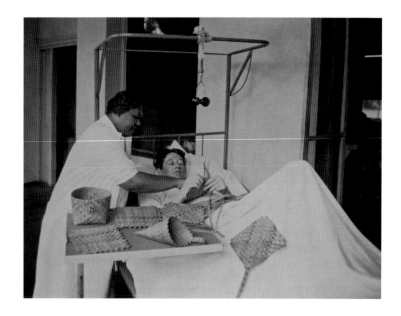

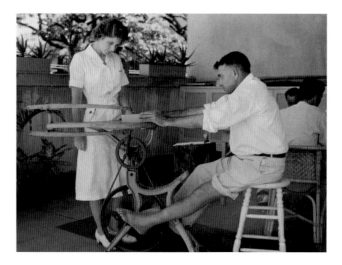

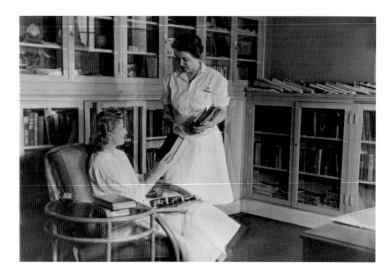

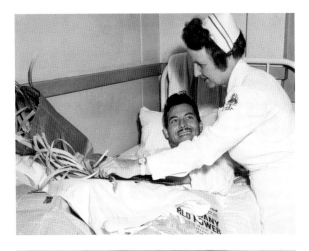

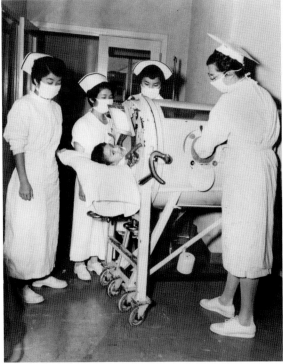

and occupational therapy mere 'busywork.'"[66] While many doctors felt it didn't hurt, they couldn't be bothered with writing referrals. There was similar resistance to physical therapy and speech therapy before they gained the acceptance enjoyed today.

Physical therapy (PT) got its start at the hospital in the 1920s with diathermy and massage treatments. In 1955, equipment used in the treatment of severe polio cases was extensive, and included hot pack machines, respirators, three-way mirrors, stationary bicycles, practice stairs and parallel bars, sandbags, weights, roller skates, braces, crutches, and a cyclotherapy table with rotary vibrator apparatus to stimulate circulation. Physical therapists also had at their disposal diathermy machines, infrared and ultraviolet ray lamps, a whirlpool, paraffin vat, and electrical stimulator. These therapies prevented thousands of polio patients—who ranged from babies to adults in their forties—from remaining crippled. Hydrotherapy was also used for the neurotic, alcoholic, postoperative, and postencephalitis patients and for burn cases.

Today, one or a combination of rehabilitation therapies are a standard feature of care for physical and cognitive injuries, diseases, and surgeries, covering all types of inpatients, outpatients, and homecare patients.

Orthopedics

The first orthopedic surgery room was established in 1923 after Frank Greenwell donated the funds in memory of his mother, Elizabeth Caroline Greenwell. However, the earliest existing record of an orthopedic condition at The Queen's Hospital dates to an 1871 patient report, which cites a fractured arm and the death of "a native from disease of the hip joint." An 1883 report tells of an operation "for stretching the ulnar nerve" and another mentions the "excision of the elbow joint."[67]

During the 1920s, a new type of lighter plaster for casts was introduced. In the 1930s and 1940s, male orthopedic patients were placed in twelve- to fourteen-bed wards on Liholiho 1. Many had osteomyelitis (infection of the bone), which made long hospital stays necessary. The first orthopedic unit, a twelve-bed male ward, was opened in the old Pauahi Wing in 1946. In the 1940s, Dr. Ralph Cloward established a one-man bone bank at Queen's with the cooperation of the Blood Bank. The bone bank, the first in the United

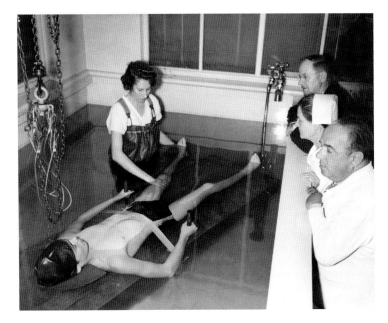

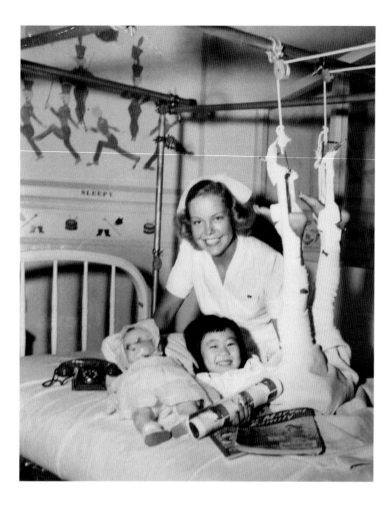

The procedure involved removal of a damaged disc using a "Cloward drill" and placing dowel-shaped bone grafts in the holes to fuse the spine. He also devised a method of operating on the cervical discs via the throat, known as the "Cloward procedure." Cloward devised over a hundred specialized surgical instruments. He served as chief of neurosurgery at both Queen's and Kuakini hospitals and published scores of articles in medical journals. Dr. Cloward died at age ninety-two, still internationally known for his innovations and brilliance.

Currently, the Department of Orthopedics keeps the operating rooms busy with 5,700 cases a year, representing about 29 percent of all surgeries at Queen's and performing the majority of joint replacements on Oʻahu. Recent improvements include a specially trained orthopedic nursing staff and standardized protocols that improve outcomes for joint replacement and spine surgery. New technology provides three-dimensional imaging during surgery, which allows precision never before possible. The combination of current technology and surgeons with a spectrum of orthopedic subspecialties drives the most difficult cases to Queen's.

A New Home for Nurses

In 1931, Mrs. Henry (Rebecca) Lapham of Chicago, a frequent visitor to Hawaiʻi, noticed the three meager cottages provided for nurses at Queen's. The hospital could not afford to construct new quarters, so when Mrs. Lapham returned home, she wrote to philanthropist Edward S. Harkness, who agreed to donate $125,000 (approximately $1.76 million in 2008 dollars) toward a new nurses' home, provided that the sum be matched by local grants.

Designed by C. W. Dickey, the Harkness Nurses' Home was ready for occupancy by May 1932. The *Honolulu Star-Bulletin* reported that "the new dormitory bears many resemblances to a well-appointed club," and that many of

States, was used for Cloward's spinal fusion technique, which became world renowned.

Born in Salt Lake City, Utah, Ralph Bingham Cloward (1908–2000) earned his medical degree at Rush Medical School in Chicago in 1934. After completing his neurology and neurosurgical training at Billings Memorial Hospital and the University of Chicago Clinics in 1938, he moved to Honolulu. There he began his neurology and neurosurgery practice. For his services after the Pearl Harbor attack on December 7, 1941, Cloward received the highest civilian commendation from President Franklin D. Roosevelt. He traveled from one hospital to the next, operating from early morning to late at night, and as the only neurosurgeon in the Pacific, he was assigned to remain in Honolulu for the duration of the war, working seven days a week treating Pacific Theater casualties.

Dr. Cloward's main interest was the spine. He performed his first posterior lumbar interbody fusion (PLIF) in 1943.

its features, like balconies and recessed spaces, give "a real Hawaiian atmosphere as well as a feeling of shade and comfort."[68] The $250,000 dormitory accommodated three superintendents of nurses, a "house mother," sixteen supervisory nurses, thirty-nine graduate nurses, and sixty-six student nurses, for a total of 125 people. Superintendents had suites with a living room, bedroom, and bath. Each pair of supervisors' rooms had connecting baths. A swimming pool and volleyball court were also included for the benefit of nurses during their hours of recreation. In 1939, an addition known today as the Harkness Annex was built to accommodate eighty more nurses. Twenty-four nurses living in a frame building and fifty living off hospital grounds were housed in the addition. A dining room was built for nurses on the ground floor. After The Queen's Hospital School of Nursing closed, it became a general cafeteria for staff and visitors. Although referred to as the Harkness Dining Room, its official name is the Rebecca Lapham Dining Hall. Today, Harkness is used for administrative offices. The 1932 cage door elevator is still in use, and is probably the oldest elevator in operation in Honolulu.

The Harkness Nurses' Home
as it appears today. Used for
hospital administration, the
structure is now referred to
as the Harkness Building.

The lobby of the Harkness Nurses' Home, 1935.

opposite
Harriet R. Delamere Library for nurses in the
Harkness Nurses' Home, circa 1930s.

Puʻuhonua, the Mental Health Clinic

In 1935, Dr. Nils Larsen wrote, "we have grown toward that
ideal that a hospital is a place where people come to have
their illnesses and disease problems properly analyzed. It
is the constant addition of necessary equipment that has
enabled us to give more and more of that type of service."[69]
Progress in the late 1930s included the addition of a new isolation room and an expanded maternity department. In 1938,
The Queen's Hospital had 300 beds, 400 employees, and admitted 9,409 patients who stayed an average of 9.05 days.

Also in 1938, the Territory of Hawai'i built a demonstration "mental hygiene" unit called the Hawai'i Mental Health Clinic at the *mauka*, or mountain, end of the Lihohiho Wing, reflecting a trend toward scientific and humane treatment of the mentally ill. The one-year trial led to a Bureau of Mental Hygiene under the Board of Health,[70] which operated the unit until 1946, when The Queen's Hospital took over and named it Pu'uhonua ("place of refuge").

Pu'uhonua was remodeled in the 1950s with an enclosed courtyard and twenty-five beds. From the Liholiho Wing, one occasionally saw a nurse from Pu'uhonua, with white uniform, nurse's hat, white stockings, and white leather shoes,

running after a patient. The cinderblock wall enclosing the courtyard was only 6 feet high, and an agile patient could escape by making a running leap at the wall. Jean Grippin, RN, who worked in Pu'uhonua in the early 1970s, remembers a large tree in the middle of the courtyard.[71] In the evening, a cacophony of screeching mynah birds could be heard throughout the unit—a gift from Dr. Hillebrand, who introduced the bird to Hawai'i from India in the 1860s. The unit and its patients were moved to Kekela in 1973. Both Pu'uhonua and the Liholiho Wing were razed in 1982 to make way for the Queen Emma Tower.

Mabel Leilani Smyth Memorial Building

The Mabel Leilani Smyth Memorial Building, completed in 1941, was built in honor of a nurse known as the Florence Nightingale of Hawai'i. From early childhood, Mabel Smyth longed to become a nurse. Originally from Kona on the island of Hawai'i, she attended Springfield Hospital Training School for Nurses in Massachusetts, and became the first woman of Hawaiian ancestry to earn certification in public health. From 1918 to 1927, Smyth served as head nurse at Palama Settlement. She was known for her quiet wisdom, executive abilities, gracious dignity, and human understanding.[72] Smyth introduced modern public health nursing to Honolulu. In 1927, she became the first director of the Department of Public Health Nursing at the Territorial Board of Health. Consolidating two branches of nursing, she directed the formation of a department of general public health nursing and extended this service to rural O'ahu and the other Hawaiian islands.

Her untimely death at age forty-three in 1936 was caused by an embolism following surgery to remove a broken sewing needle. The needle, embedded in her chest since she was ten, always worried her, although doctors felt it was unnecessary to remove it. A shocked and saddened community came together to construct a multiuse building as a memorial to Mabel Smyth. Dr. Douglas Bell, president of the City and County Medical Society, suggested a merging of the Nursing Service Bureau, the Physicians' Exchange, the Hawai'i Medical Library, and other related offices in the proposed building. Over $90,000 was raised in a fund drive, and The Queen's Hospital provided the small, triangular lot on the corner of Beretania and Punchbowl streets.

C. W. Dickey brought his unique style to the building, dovetailing its design with his other buildings at Queen's. Decorations on the building depict the Hawaiian *'ape* leaf (elephant ear) in concrete over the windows and walls, intertwined with the medical profession's staff of Asclepius (or Aessculapius) over the door. Said in Hawaiian lore to ward

The Queen's Conference Center (formerly known as the Mabel Leilani Smyth Memorial Buidling).

Hospital Day at The Queen's Hospital, 1940. First celebrated
nationally in 1921, Hospital Day also commemorates the
anniversary of the birth of Florence Nightingale on
May 12, 1820.

off evil spirits, the *'ape* was planted near gates or the leaves were placed under the mats of the sick. Dedicated on January 4, 1941, the building would take on an unexpected role when the Japanese attacked Pearl Harbor on December 7 of that year. Listed on the National Register of Historic Places and registered with the State Historic Preservation Office, the Mabel Smyth Building was renovated and reopened in 2001 as The Queen's Conference Center, an education and conferencing facility. The newly appointed auditorium retains the name Mabel Smyth.

Meanwhile, an organization that would be critically important during the war was also planning its home on the Queen's campus. The Honolulu Blood-Plasma Bank (known as the Blood Bank of Hawai'i since 1946) was established in February 1941. Its building was located near the Rebecca Lapham Dining Hall. With advancements in blood banking science, more laboratory space was required, so the Blood Bank later moved to its current facility on Dillingham Boulevard. The building at Queen's was razed in 1978 to make way for the underground Nā'ea Radiation Therapy facility.

THE MODERN AGE OF MEDICINE

Aerial view of Queen's during World War II, circa 1944.
Red crosses were painted on the roof of the Bishop and
Liholiho wings identifying Queen's as a hospital.

The War Years

Although World War II raged abroad, the United States remained officially neutral. If the committee of Queen's doctors that gathered at the Internes' [sic] Cottage in the middle of the day on September 24, 1941 was concerned about the war, there is no recorded indication of it. They were assembled to discuss crowding at Queen's and possible ways to expand. Dr. Nils Larsen, medical director, rattled off the number of major and minor surgeries for the three months of summer in 1938, 1940, and 1941. The numbers showed an increase in major surgeries by almost 23 percent and minor surgeries by 44 percent in two years. "I certainly think Surgery is very badly in need of more space," said Dr. Joseph Strode. "The present rooms have been patched up so many times that they are a disgrace to The Queen's Hospital, and I am ashamed to bring mainland doctors . . . through our present rooms."[73] The hospital also needed more beds and staff. A local newspaper reported that the desk nurse was forced to keep new patients in the hallways or the emergency room on gurneys or wheelchairs until space could be found for them the next day.[74] Placing patients on the lanai was considered, but only as a last resort, since it could only be done "in cases of external physical injury, fractures, contusions, *etc.*"[75] Plans for a one-hundred-bed four-story wing were drawn up by architect C. W. Dickey, and a federal grant for $250,000 was secured. On December 4, 1941, a fund drive was announced to cover the remainder of the cost.

The morning of Sunday, December 7 began like any other. Although World War II had been raging since 1939, most people were not overly worried that Hawai'i could become a front line in the war. Still, there were preparations. There had been a major build-up of U.S. military power in Hawai'i in 1940, and Queen's had ample medical supplies on hand. On the day the fund drive was announced, Dr. John J. Moorhead, a veteran of World War I and an expert on trauma surgery, arrived to give island doctors an intensive course on the treatment of war injuries. He began to deliver a second talk at the Mabel Smyth Memorial Building on the morning of December 7.

Early that Sunday morning, a plane zoomed low over the hospital. A nurse in the mental health ward said to another, "Well, there goes the Navy." One patient stood up and said,

"Gee, those planes look strange to me. I don't think they are American jobs." The nurses paid no attention and went about their duties. Another nurse came on duty looking pale and ill. She quickly pulled the two nurses into the office. "My God, haven't you heard?" she exclaimed. "[The Japanese] are bombing the island. They've downed ships in Pearl Harbor. It's a mass of flames."[76] The nurse went on to say that her boyfriend had been strafed by machine gun fire from a Japanese plane while walking along a country road, but wasn't hurt badly and made it to a plantation hospital for treatment. Meanwhile, Mrs. J. B. Steele, a navy wife who was in the hospital for observation, heard the planes overhead and explosions in the distance. She knew there were no navy maneuvers on Sunday, so she suspected immediately that it was an attack.[77]

At the Mabel Smyth Memorial Building, Dr. Moorhead had barely begun to speak when a local doctor rushed in to say that twelve surgeons were needed immediately at the army's Tripler Hospital. In the audience was Dr. Joseph Strode, who drove Moorhead to Tripler in his car. Together with other civilian and military doctors, Strode and Moorhead spent the next eleven hours in the operating room, each joining one of eight teams treating hundreds of casualties flooding in from Pearl Harbor. They would work for the next ten days. Among the surgeons helping at Tripler was Dr. Ralph Cloward, who performed over forty craniotomies in four days. He would later describe the head wounds: "Nearly all these wounds were compound depressed fractures of the skull produced by fragments of shrapnel which varied in size from thin flat pieces less than 1 cm. across to large, heavy, irregular chunks of steel 3.5 to 4 cm. wide and 0.5 to 1 cm. in thickness. The larger pieces of metal all had extremely sharp, jagged points, which ripped great irregular holes in the tissues of the head through which they passed."[78]

Bombs fell within a block of The Queen's Hospital, and, according to Steele, "doctors and nurses were running everywhere, calming patients with the surest means at hand— a hypo."[79] Casualties began pouring into Queen's. Frances Campbell, a Honolulu resident at the time, recalls: "When we passed, [Queen's] was admitting wounded citizens from many points on Oahu. . . . Emergency stations had mushroomed in parks . . . wounded were being tended on the

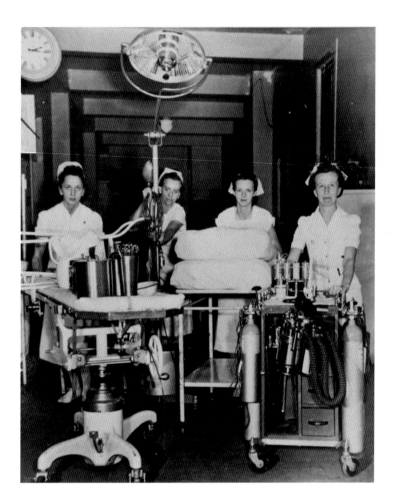

Queen's nurses trained for emergencies throughout World War II. Evacuations ramps for patients and staff were built onto the various wings at Queen's in case the hospital was bombed. The ramp shown below connected to the second floor of the Nalani Wing.

opposite
Left: Nurses and other medical staff were required to carry gas masks after the 1941 Pearl Harbor attack. *Right:* Twelve fully equipped fire trucks were placed at strategic points throughout the hospital during the war. The trucks were manned by employees trained to extinguish incendiary bombs.

open ground. All hospitals were cleared of "old" patients who could be sent home safely."[80] Over one hundred beds at Queen's were vacated within hours to accept casualties. According to Marcelle Young, a Queen's nurse, electricity stopped at about the time the first patients arrived, shutting down elevators and forcing staff to scramble up and down stairways. "Patients crowded the halls, and medics made makeshift beds by putting stretchers across desks," she said.[81] Young tried to help a man whose abdomen was "blown apart," but he died as she tried to stop the bleeding.

The nurses listened as a radio announcer warned that another attack could come at any minute. "Not a light must show in these islands come nightfall," he said in a voice strained with anxiety.[82] Everyone at the hospital was learning about the sinking ships at Pearl Harbor, and how Wheeler, Hickam, Schofield, and the Kaneohe Naval Air Station had been hit simultaneously. Billowing smoke could be seen coming from Pearl Harbor. Nurses busied themselves with making bandages and putting blue cellophane over

flashlight bulbs in preparation for the blackout, while attendants came with canvas to black out doorways and windows. With bus service canceled, many hospital staff spent the night on cots in the basement. At Mabel Smyth, several private duty nurses spent the first few nights in the lounge. The husband of one of these nurses was assigned to make wooden boxes to bury the dead a few blocks away and would come back late to Mabel Smyth to catch a few hours of sleep.

The Blood Bank conducted a campaign that brought thousands of volunteers to Queen's to give blood and to volunteer. Martial law was declared, and the military governor issued an order that all graduate nurses register with the Office of Civilian Defense at the Mabel Smyth Memorial Building. For three days, hundreds of nurses showed up to be registered, fingerprinted, and to receive passes to travel to and from work during blackout hours. Gas masks were also issued to hospital personnel. The plate glass doors of the building were taped to prevent flying glass from a bomb hit, and prisoners dug slit trenches in the yard. Plans were put in place

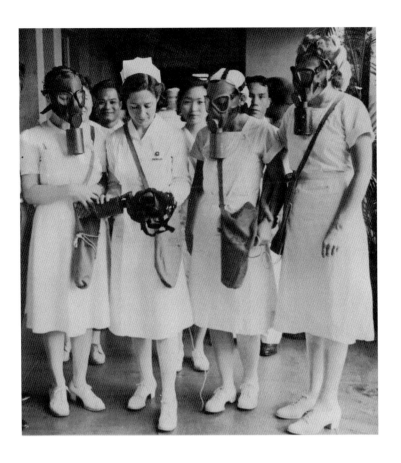

to turn Mabel Smyth into a hospital in case of overflow or bombing of The Queen's Hospital. Instructions were written for the setting up of emergency cots, and the hospital sent over large boxes of supplies. At the hospital, wooden evacuation ramps resembling adult-sized sliding boards were constructed from all wings of the hospital for patients and staff.

Dr. Moorhead would stay until December 30. In combination with his wound cleaning techniques, he recommended the use of sulfanilamide, a sulfur-based drug effective against infection, to dress wounds.[83] Although not an antibiotic (penicillin would come later), sulfanilamide is credited with saving many wounded at Pearl Harbor. In his farewell address to physicians, Moorhead said, "Honolulu has been the proving ground for the technique of handling war wounds. I shall recommend that this technique be adopted universally throughout the country." He added, "The United States of America owes you, the civilian doctors of Honolulu, a debt of gratitude for the work you did on December 7th."[84]

Plans for the new wing were set aside due to the federal government's freezing of building materials. Not until late 1943 were building materials released for essential projects, and construction of the new wing finally got underway in 1944. Continuing the tradition of naming buildings after historically significant people, the board named the new structure Kīna'u, after Elizabeth Kīna'u, mother of King Kamehameha IV. However, the hospital managed to have class rooms constructed for the School of Nursing in 1943 before construction of Kīna'u commenced. Halekula, which means "school house," was considered a temporary wartime building. The nurses described it as "a beautiful dream" come true. A "good deal of time" was spent everyday locking and unlocking the building's sixteen doors and eighty-two windows, but the nurses felt it was worth it "just to have ample space in which to spread out and carry on our business in an efficient manner."[85] Halekula didn't turn out to be so temporary; it survived as a termite-ridden building until it was demolished in 1962. The current Hawai'i Medical Library was built in its place.

THE MODERN AGE OF MEDICINE

Working in the linen room, Kaimuki Girl Scouts help make Santa apple tray decorations for patients at Queen's in December 1943.

right
Doris Goto (center, at table) works with a bolt of material, while Mrs. Yamada (far right) and other seamstresses sew nurses' uniforms, 1941.

The Queen's Carpenter Shop in 1942. *Left to right*: Mr. Suzuki, Kenso Hamada, Kazuo Otsuki, and Richard Yamaguchi.

below
Pastry chef Charles Agcaoili in the hospital bakery, circa 1940s.

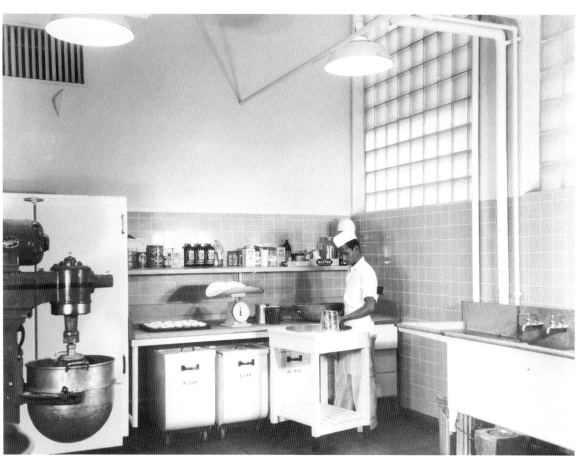

The Kīna'u Wing was built to the right of Nalani, extending the long façade of The Queen's Hospital's frontage. In this photo, taken in 1946, the view includes Nalani in the center, and the Kīna'u Wing on the right. The updated 1905 Pauahi wing is out of view on the left.

opposite
New maternity suite, 1948.

Uniforms Bring Sense of Order

While Kīna'u was being built, there was certainly some disorder with patients waiting in hallways and construction going full bore outside, but there was still a great deal of order at The Queen's Hospital. The inside of the hospital was antiseptic and aseptic, and was run as tightly as ever with overcrowding and war rationing, and as much as the current age is a casual one, the 1940s was a formal one, at least as far as uniforms were concerned.

Each profession had its own uniform; there were so many types that the *Queen's Messenger* felt it necessary to catalog them. The "graduate registered nurse" was of course the most recognizable, with her crisp, white uniform, white shoes and stockings, and a cap with the pin of her nursing school. In addition to a school pin, registered nurses were permitted to wear the Red Cross pin, which was to be worn "at the collar…or on the left, over the heart." A Red Cross nurse could wear her pin with street clothes only while on professional business. No other jewelry or pins were permitted. Student nurses wore green and white, but a pink dress with white collar and cuffs was added for the student "infants' nurse" during the first two months of training, followed by a white cap with a pink band.

Attendants trained through the National Youth Administration Program for Hospital Attendants, a federal program, wore Hoover-type dresses in yellow, which apparently earned them the nickname "Canaries." "Maids," who were the housekeepers, wore a dark blue dress with a white collar, while social service workers wore (over street clothes) a starched, white smock with "S.S." in blue letters. While inside the hospital, registered occupational therapists wore a white uniform with the American Occupational Therapy Association arm insignia and a gold pin, adding a navy blue jacket with the OT pin in front for outdoors.[86]

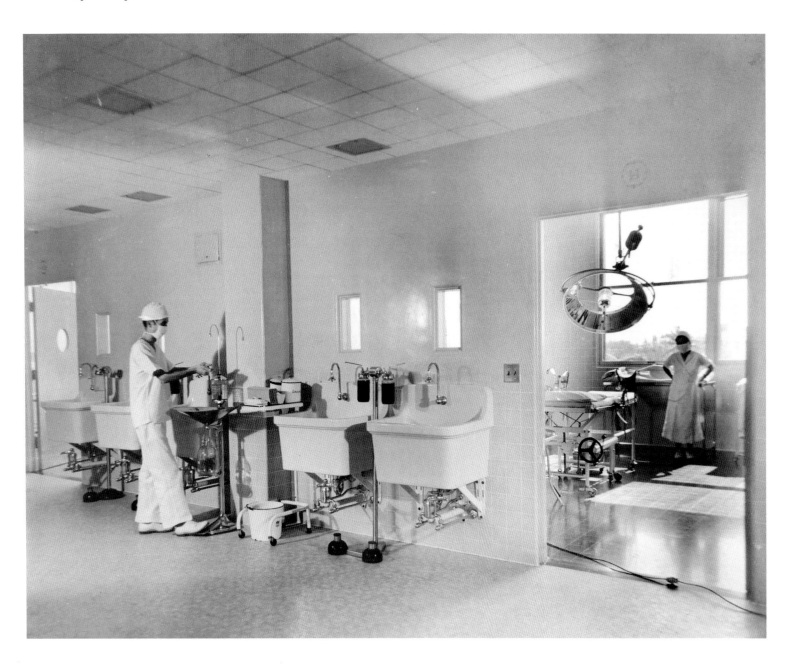

The Kīnaʻu Wing

The Kīnaʻu Wing was built to the right of Nalani, extending the long façade of The Queen's Hospital's frontage. In 1945, a visitor facing the front of the hospital would have seen the old 1905 Pauahi on the left (with an updated façade), Nalani in the center, and Kīnaʻu on the right. The other two major wings, Bishop and Liholiho, were not visible from the front, since they ran behind Nalani and perpendicular to it. The cost of the Kīnaʻu Wing was approximately $820,000 (about $8 million in 2008 dollars).[87] Additional expenses were also required in 1945, including the removal of the evacuation ramps built on each wing of the hospital at the outbreak of the war.[88]

On March 17, 1945, the second floor of Kīnaʻu opened for patients, and in a matter of days, its thirty-nine beds were occupied. The floor had both private and group rooms. Not every area in the building was opened at the same time, or even in the same year. The 1945 Queen's Annual Report described the reinforced concrete structure as "a thoroughly good building," owing to the fact that it was "pre-war quality in everything except some plumbing fixtures and other metal finishing for which wartime substitutes had to be accepted." Because the hospital insisted on prewar materials, "work has purposely proceeded slowly and the unit will not be completed until the latter part of 1946."[89]

Thirty patients were moved from Pauahi 1 to three of four ten-bed wards on Kīnaʻu 1. The new operating rooms were located on Kīnaʻu 3, as were maternity and birth services. The entire third floor of the adjoining Nalani Wing was also devoted to maternity. The fourth floor, with fourteen private rooms of the "semi-luxury type," was not opened that year due to a nursing shortage. Upon the completion of Kīnaʻu, Queen's total bed count was 440.

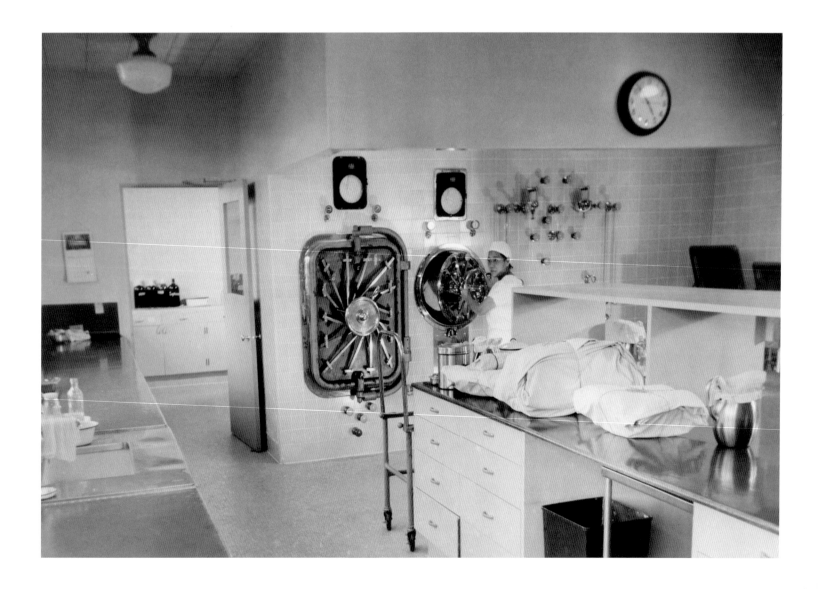

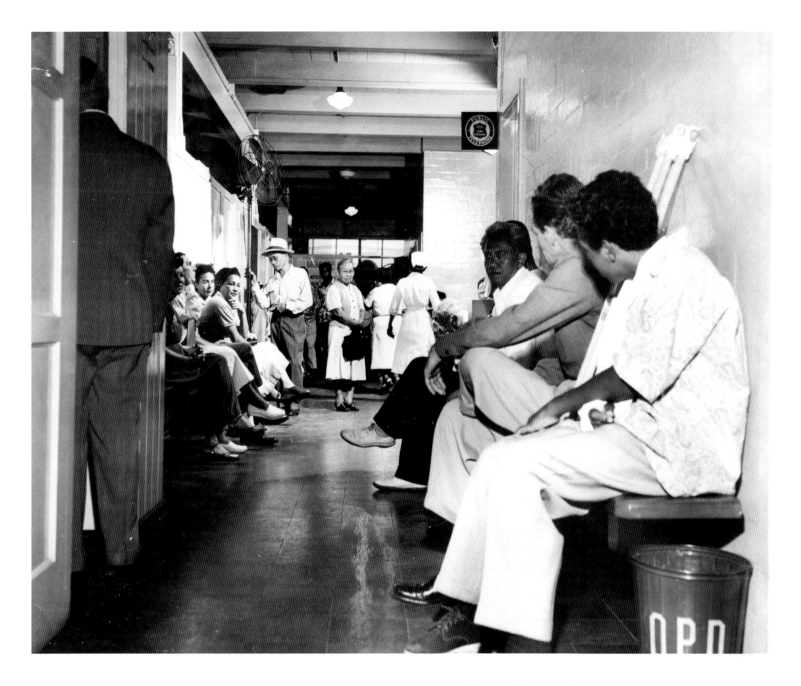

Patients wait at the Out-Patient Department (now known as the Queen Emma Clinics), circa 1947. Under government contract, medical care was provided for those who were unable to pay for all or part of their care.

opposite
Helen Morikawa, RN, in the Kīna'u 3 utility room of the Obstetrics Division, where equipment was sterilized.

Care to the Disadvantaged

Two years after the Kīna'u Wing was completed, the Out-Patient Department (OPD) was created.[90] The OPD continues to play a significant role at the hospital to this day. Now known as the Queen Emma Clinics (QEC), the OPD opened on July 28, 1947 in a detached structure on Punchbowl Street between the driveway entrance and the Miller Street corner. In the mid-1920s Dr. Nils Larsen had become closely allied with Palama Settlement, which developed clinics to improve the health of the people in the district. In 1947, much of the

medical clinic work was turned over to The Queen's Hospital and St. Francis Hospital under government contract. The OPD would provide general health and specialized medical care for those who were unable to pay for all or part of their care. In the first month, 1,156 patients were treated. There were originally thirteen clinics, including Diabetic; Pediatric; Heart; Maternal Health; Gynecology; and Ear, Nose, and Throat. The OPD was staffed by residents and interns with an attending physician to oversee the work, as it is today. In 1952, an OPD Annex opened in the Pauahi Wing's first floor. When the first two floors of a new Pauahi were completed in 1960, the entire OPD moved into the ground floor (with the exception of the Dental Clinic, which is still the only program in Hawai'i that serves special needs patients, emergency room patients, prisoners, the disabled, and the economically disadvantaged). When the Same Day Surgery

Center moved into this space in 1999, the department, now called the Queen Emma Clinics, moved into the ground floor of the Queen Emma Tower. Today, about 10 percent of QEC patients have commercial insurance, but most are covered under the State Med-Quest program, Medicare, Medicaid or are uninsured. QEC is the major site for residents of the UH/Hawai'i Residency Programs, Inc. In 2008, the clinics had 31,995 visits and offered the services of twenty-six general and specialty clinics.

Victories over Infectious Diseases

While public hygiene had improved and immunology was established as a science in the nineteenth century, drug therapy had few outstanding victories in the first half of the twentieth century, and infection remained a serious problem. The late Dr. Charles Judd remembered that when he visited

Queen's in the 1920s with his parents as a child, the "over-powering smell of antiseptic was tremendous." He noted that "the key causes of death were pneumonia and tuberculosis."[91]

Early in the century, Salvarsan was used effectively against the early stages of syphilis. However, many years passed without significant gains in drug therapy until sulfanilamide became available. Queen's first used it to treat gonorrhea in 1937, and it was used to prevent the infection of wounds during the war. These drugs would be eclipsed by antibiotics. The first antibiotic, penicillin, came to Hawai'i in 1943, but it was only available to the military. By 1944, penicillin was made available to civilians, and The Queen's Hospital was designated as the distribution center. At first, scientists scrambled to produce mass quantities of penicillin, and then they began to search for other antibiotics, which led to the discovery of streptomycin in 1944. Commercially produced streptomycin, which reached Hawai'i in 1946, was effective against tuberculosis. When given to patients at Leahi Hospital, it had remarkable results. Some who were considered too ill for even streptomycin recovered. Soon after, leprosy was defeated by a multidrug therapy that included an antibiotic and sulfones. Although antibiotics are not effective against viruses, they ushered in a new era in the treatment of infectious diseases. At the end of the 1940s, there must have been a sense of hope and new beginnings at The Queen's Hospital. The war had ended in victory on August 15, 1945, the Kīna'u Wing was complete, and antibiotics had turned the tide against many diseases.

opposite and below
Queen's coffee shop, 1949. Esther Pyun, occupational therapist, and Nobuko Kaneda, social worker, were the first customers at the new coffee shop; administrator Carl I. Flath serves them. *Below:* Loretta Woo and Juanita Light enjoy coffee shop classics— a hot fudge sundae, hamburger, and Coca Cola.

The Harkness Nurses' Home, 1940.

THE TRAINING SCHOOL FOR NURSES

The Queen's Hospital was established during the period when Florence Nightingale pioneered modern nursing and elevated the profession to one of respect. Her Nightingale School for Nurses opened in 1860. After the first trained nurse—a part Hawaiian woman named Mary Adams—came in 1886, the hospital hired more trained nurses and had eight by 1888.[1] The first graduate nurses were Miss Margaret Carroll, head nurse, and Miss Nina Cook, assistant head nurse; both came in 1892. A third graduate nurse, Miss Kate Harris, was added as a night nurse. By 1909, the position of superintendent of nurses was created. Nurses were "to wait upon the patients, soothing them and applying their wants, reporting to the doctors and carrying out their orders, . . . attend to the cleaning of the building, the mending, sewing, and washing of the bedding and the table linen of the Hospital and the clothing of the patients."[2] There were two shifts—7:00 A.M. and 7:00 P.M.—and not much time for breaks or time off. As the profession of nursing developed, nonclinical work such as sewing, washing, and cleaning were delegated to others, and more reasonable working hours were instituted.

The core of the nursing profession was characterized by individuals who were devoted to patients and who were loyal to their profession. Margaret Jones, a Queen's nurse beloved by the community, followed the sacrificial example of Florence Nightingale. During World War I, Miss Jones accompanied a widowed expectant mother to England, hoping to arrive before the birth. In 1915, they sailed on the ill-fated *Lusitania*, which was torpedoed by a German submarine; 1,198 lives were lost. Miss Jones was said to have given her life preserver and place in the lifeboat to her patient.

Before The Queen's Hospital Training School for Nurses (later called The Queen's Hospital School of Nursing) was established in 1916, most graduate nurses were recruited from the mainland United States. A letter to Miss Ida Shannon from Queen's superintendent Johannes F. Eckardt, dated January 6, 1912, outlines an offer of employment after the nurse arrived on Quarantine Island (now known as Sand Island):

The Hospital employs graduate nurses only. . . . They receive $50.00 a month, with board, lodging and free laundry, have an afternoon off duty each week and an hour each afternoon and when coming off night duty, they have a full week off duty.[3]

The Queen's Hospital School of Nursing (and other Hawai'i nursing schools) helped make it possible for Hawai'i to produce its own supply of homegrown nurses who would work in all corners of the territory. In the 1920s, the wards were under the supervision of one graduate nurse assisted by three student nurses and two orderlies. Nurses had an average of nineteen patients to look after.[4] In 1935, the eight-hour day was introduced. Before modern advancements and specialization of nurses came, nursing was a labor-intensive profession. Barbara Ideta, a 1956 graduate of Queen's School of Nursing, recalled that student nurses went to Central Supply to learn to sharpen needles before improved technology made it possible to mass produce them.[5] Before the age of disposables, items such as glass intravenous bottles and syringes and rubber intravenous tubing were sterilized and reused. Ethel Matsui, also a 1956 graduate, said that nurses did everything. They changed beds, gave meds, started IVs, and gave back rubs before bed. Each nurse was in charge of an entire ward of ten patients with a practical nurse (or orderly in the men's wards) as an assistant.[6] Elaine Kawamoto, a 1964 graduate, indicated little had changed in the 1960s.[7] During the day shift, a head nurse (now called a nurse manager), six nurses, and a ward clerk (unit secretary) took care of a whole floor. During the night shift, one nurse and a shared nurses' aide took care of twenty-two patients.

"We were jacks-of-all-trades in the old days," said Kawamoto. "Nurses did their own oxygen for asthmatics with

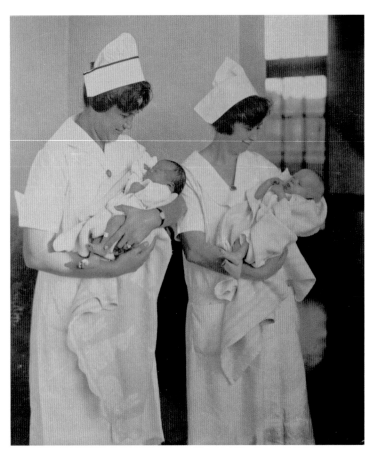

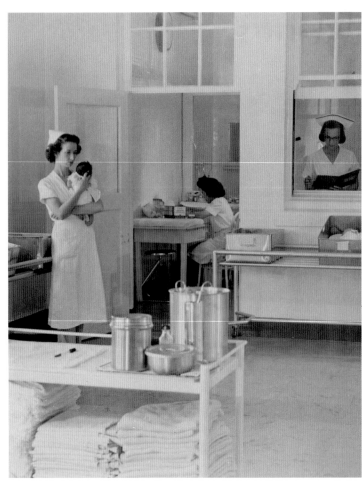
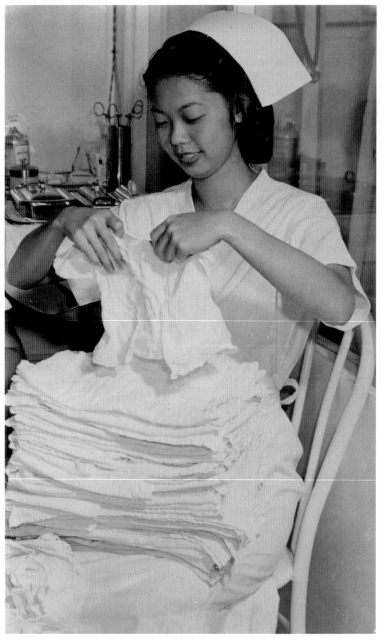

opposite, clockwise from top left
Queen's maternity nurses, circa 1920s.

Student nurses Patricia Anderson and Catherine Sims prepare bottles for the nursery on Nalani 3, circa 1940.

Florence Ohama-Ching as a Queen's student nurse in 1948. She graduated in the class of 1950.

Queen's nursery, circa 1940.

below

Nurses help to beautify the grounds in front of the Harkness Nurses' Home, circa 1933.

The Queen's Hospital School of Nursing class of 1941. In front (left to right) are Helen Kubota, Glenna Kimura, Rosie Kim, Fraida Bojko, and Leatrice Koiushi. In back are Nancy Horikawa, Florence Loo, Grace Abshire, Catherine Sims, and Patricia Anderson.

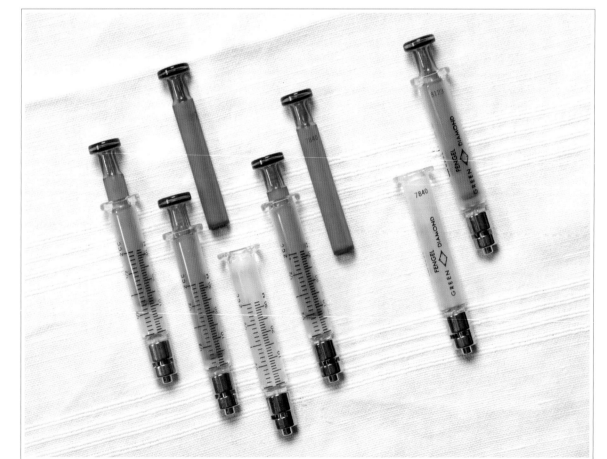

Fengel Corporation Green Diamond all glass 2cc. hypodermic syringes, circa 1940s.

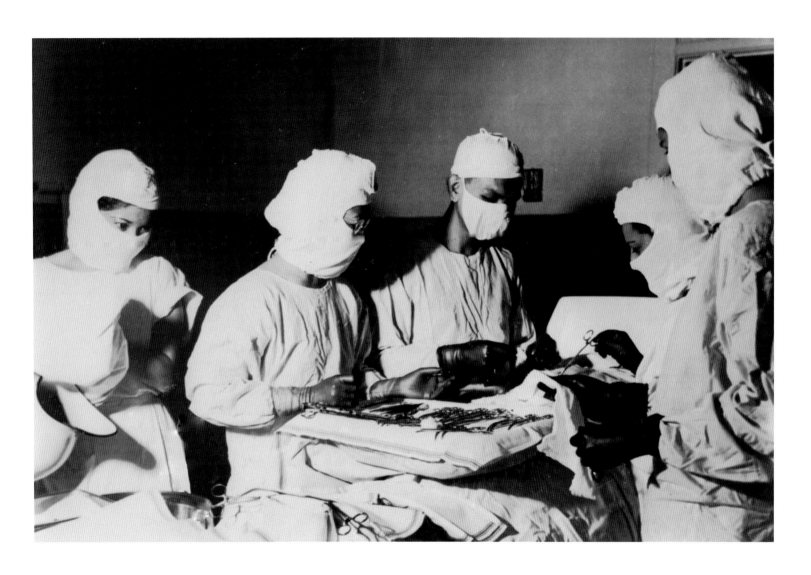

Queen's doctors and nurses prepare to perform surgery, 1945.

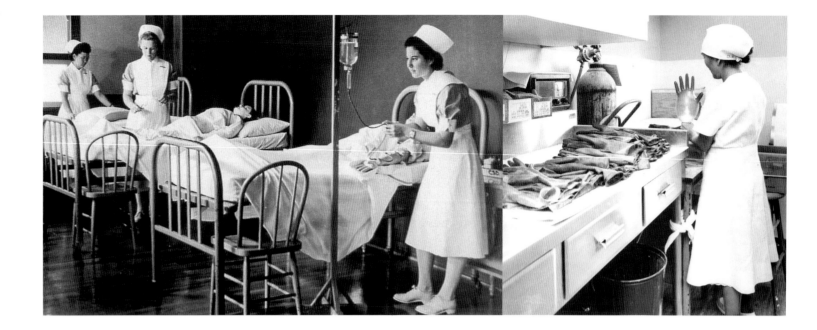

oxygen tents—there was no respiratory therapy." Kawamoto says that they put patients with skin diseases like eczema in a bathtub and "scrubbed them down with Aveeno (ground oatmeal) to get the dead skin off and then wrapped them with Saran wrap from the kitchen."[8] They mixed formula for infants with the kitchen's blender and retrieved medications from the pharmacy at night when there was no pharmacist on duty. Nurses also scrubbed down bedpans, bath basins, and emesis basins (for vomit and teeth brushing), then put them in an autoclave for sterilization. There were no housekeepers at night until the chief administrator happened to see Kawamoto up on a ladder early one morning at the end of her shift cleaning the walls of a room to prepare it for the next patient. There were no intensive care units (ICUs) in the 1950s; the first units opened at Queen's in the 1960s.

Ankle-length uniforms had given way to uniforms that were just below the knee by the 1950s, but the formality remained. Nurses were required to wear their hats and nursing pins. The white uniforms had to be spotless, with equally clean oxford leather shoes with clean laces, and hair was worn off the collar. (Pants suits were allowed beginning in 1970 at Queen's.) Formality dictated that nurses be addressed as "Miss" or "Mrs."

Nursing was traditionally seen as a profession for women, but that perception has changed. Although some accounts refer to J. P. Rodrigues as the first male nurse at Queen's, he

Student nurses of The Queen's Hospital School of Nursing train on mannequins, circa 1940s.

Masae Ayson tests gloves for leaks and defects in the new glove room, 1955.

opposite
Nurses perform safety drills, circa late 1950s.

was actually the purveyor, one of whose many functions was head nurse. Men did work in the hospital in early times, but they were considered orderlies. The first male graduate nurse to work at Queen's was a Mr. Yen Chin in 1912. He left within a year to work at the Oʻahu Insane Asylum, which apparently paid more. Chin had two brothers who were also nurses; both worked at the Territorial (now State) Hospital in Kāneʻohe. The first male nurse to graduate from The Queen's Hospital School of Nursing was Eugene Lee in 1959. By the 1990s, a male nurse, Duane Walker, served as vice president of nursing. Although female nurses still outnumber males, most people today would not give a male nurse a second thought.

Changes in nursing accelerated toward the end of the twentieth century. In 1974, nurses at Queen's unionized.[9] By the 1980s, patient care had become more complicated. Trish Morrison, RN, vice president in charge of general

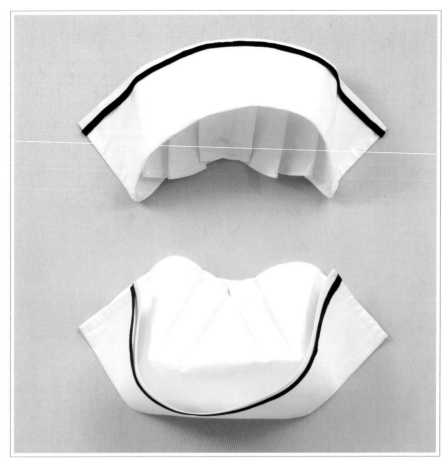

Student nurses' caps, circa 1950s. After completing six months as a freshman, a student was given a nurse's cap. Caps were washed by the student and soaked in liquid starch. The cap was placed on a mirror, refrigerator, or other flat surface to dry, then peeled off and folded. Seniors had a black stripe on their caps to denote their rank.

below
Student nurses prepare to serve as tour guides at Queen's during Hospital Day, 1953. *Left to right*: Misses C. Kinoshita, A. Okamura, M. Kawasaki, N. Kimura, S. Morioka, K. Koba, and S. Matsumoto.

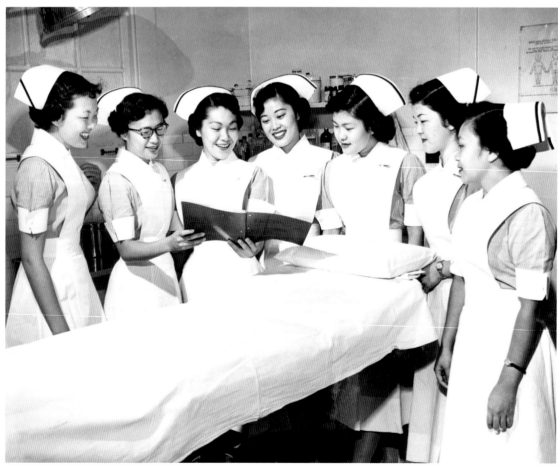

nursing at Queen's, said that the major change in nursing was "letting the nurse do what . . . they do best—take care of the patients."[10] Housekeeping duties, moving patients around, and some of the pharmaceutical work and paperwork were delegated to others not involved with direct patient care.[11] Nursing was also making a shift to "primary care nursing," which meant that one nurse planned and coordinated care during a patient's entire stay on the unit. Today, most nurses practice "total care nursing," in which each nurse drives a patient's care during his or her shift according to the needs of the patient at that time.

Queen's has encouraged professional development by establishing a four-level Clinical Ladder program that rewards clinical advancement and provides training in various specialties. Today's nurses are also encouraged to earn national certifications in specialty areas such as anesthesia, medical-surgical, gerontology, maternal-child, gastroenterology, orthopedics, bariatrics, emergency medicine, progressive care, critical care, neurology, rehabilitation, and others. Many Queen's nurses hold specialty certifications and advanced degrees.

The Queen's Hospital School of Nursing

Because of Queen's remote location in the Pacific and relatively small size, it was difficult to find qualified graduate nurses. Most had to be brought in at considerable expense. Establishing a training school for nurses was first mentioned by the trustees in 1902, but finances were stretched thin. In 1911, an endowment fund of $5,000 for the education of nurses from M. S. Grinbaum put the issue back on the table,[12] but the trustees felt the hospital was still not in a position to take action. Meanwhile, the Kauikeolani Children's Hospital established the Territory of Hawai'i's first nursing school, which operated until the late 1920s.

In 1915, Queen's was prepared to establish its own nursing school. The goal was to alleviate the shortage of graduate nurses in Honolulu and supply the hospital with the nurses it would need as it grew. Organized by Miss Agnes H. Collins, The Queen's Hospital Training School for Nurses opened in 1916. Queen's 1916 Annual Report states:

The Queen's Hospital, of Honolulu, Hawaii, is prepared to give a three years' course of training to women desirous of

Nina Cook (1861–1947)

In 1892, Miss Nina Eunice Cook had just completed her training at Children's Hospital in San Francisco. She was summoned by the superintendent of nurses, who showed her a letter from The Queen's Hospital in Honolulu announcing an opening for assistant head nurse. Miss Cook accepted a year's employment at $50 per month to be paid in U.S. gold coin.[13]

Arrangements were made for Miss Cook to travel by sailing vessel. The captain of the ship offered her his "cabin," which was just a bunk separated from the rest of the crew by a curtain. Miss Cook wondered what she had let herself into, traveling in such an unusual manner, committed to a year's service at a hospital she knew nothing about, and with no acquaintances in Hawai'i. On her arrival in Honolulu, Miss Cook was warmly greeted at Queen's, where she and the head nurse, Miss Margaret Carroll, were the first graduate nurses in Hawai'i.

Miss Nina Cook, circa 1892. Miss Cook, one of the first graduate nurses in Hawai'i, had just completed her training at Children's Hospital in San Francisco before arriving in the islands in 1892.

Miss Cook made lifelong friendships and came to love The Queen's Hospital and the islands. The aides called Miss Cook "Mama Kuke," and Miss Carroll, "Mama Kalo." Miss Carroll was very helpful to the visiting Catholic priest at Queen's, Father Valentine, who depended upon her to urge backsliding seamen to return to church—an assignment she took seriously.

When Miss Carroll left, Miss Cook became the head nurse, but in 1895, she fell in love with one of her patients, Henry Ovenden. She resigned her position to be married. After their wedding, the couple moved to Hana, Maui. When her husband died in 1906, Mrs. Nina Cook Ovenden moved back to the mainland, but when she died in 1947, she was buried in Hana next to her husband, as she had requested.

The Queen's Hospital

Training School for Nurses

HONOLULU, HAWAII.

DIPLOMA

This Certifies That *Annie Claire Kamauoha* has completed the **Three** years Course of Instruction and Practice in this Institution, and has passed with credit the required examinations, whereby she is deemed worthy the title of

Graduate Nurse

In Witness Whereof, our signatures are hereunto affixed at Honolulu, Territory of Hawaii, this *Thirty-first* day of *August* 1917.

becoming Professional Nurses. The Training School was established by the Board of Trustees in 1916 to give women desirous of becoming Professional Nurses a systematic course of training and practice ... and to meet the demands of the community for competent Nurses. The pupils of the Training School serve in Medical, Surgical, Obstetric, Gynecological, Eye and Ear, Nervous and Mental and Orthopedic Ward; in the Isolation Pavilion, in the Dressing Rooms, in the Central Diet Kitchens, and in the Surgery.[14]

The course included textbook instruction as well as demonstrations by the superintendent of nurses. Practical lectures were given by the surgical and medical staff of the hospital. However, the "main reliance" for the training was upon systematic drills in the wards, operating rooms, dressing rooms, diet kitchens, and other departments.

By the end of 1916, the Training School had twenty nurses in training and eleven probationers. The first nurse to graduate was Mrs. Annie Claire Kamauoha, since she had already received three years of training at the Kauikeolani Children's Hospital nursing school before joining the Queen's Training School. Graduating in 1917 ahead of her class, Kamauoha became the first nurse to complete professional training in Hawai'i. Queen Lili'uokalani personally "pinned" Kamauoha and suggested that the Training School adopt her personal motto, "*onipa'a*," which means "steadfast," or "resolute." "*Onipa'a*" did indeed become the motto, and the word was embossed in gold on the Training School's pin. Although there were thirty-one students, only ten graduated in the class of 1919. Collaboration with the University of Hawai'i began that year when the College of Hawai'i arranged two courses—chemistry and dietetics—at special hours that did not conflict with the students' morning work at the hospital. Two years later, the Training School became accredited. By the 1920s, the name had been changed to The Queen's Hospital School of Nursing.

Queen's Hospital Training School for Nurses graduate pin embossed with "*onipa'a*," Queen Lili'uokalani's personal motto. The pin belonged to Violet Hook and is dated May 25, 1929.

The first uniform of the Training School was an ankle-length blue dress with a white apron, stockings, and black boots. A white cap and bib were added to the uniform after a four-month probation. In the 1930s, the uniform was changed to a green dress with a white apron and a large black bow on the front. Because the bow made its way into soup bowls and coffee cups, the white bib was brought back. Nancy Kim, a 1951 graduate of The Queen's Hospital School of Nursing, remembers the green uniforms worn by new students. "They used so much starch that they could probably stand up by themselves," she recalled of her uniforms, which were washed and pressed by the hospital's housekeeping staff. After completing six months as a freshman, a stu-

dent was given a nurse's cap. Caps were washed by the student and soaked in liquid starch. The cap was placed on a mirror, refrigerator, or other flat surface to dry, then peeled off and folded. Seniors had a black stripe on their caps to denote their rank. "Each school had their own special cap," said Kim. "When you graduated, you wore your whites."[15]

In spite of the fact that there were 107 students at the School of Nursing in 1943, all uniforms were still made by the hospital's seamstresses and were pressed on the premises. Sewing for each student consisted of making eight uniforms and twelve sets of aprons, bibs, and cuffs. (Everything was made at Queen's sewing room except sheets, pillowcases, and towels.) Five ironers and two pressers handled 17,872 uniforms, 24,917 aprons, and 18,092 bibs a year.[16]

In the beginning, students' clinical duties followed the regular nursing day shift of 7:00 A.M. to 7:00 P.M., with two hours allotted for meals and rest. After completing a four-month probation, students were given an allowance of $8 a month "to cover the expense of uniforms, books and all other equipment, and is in no wise intended as full salary, the professional education being considered sufficient additional compensation."[17] The allowance was increased to $10 a month in a student's second year, and to $12 in the third. Although the clinical day was reduced to eight hours in 1935, students had to remain on call.

The nurses' residence was a "commodious building of recent construction, situated on the south side of the park." Not a convenience was overlooked, the superintendent of nurses boasted in her 1916 report, including ample room for study, rest, and recreation.[18] However, as the School of Nursing took on more students, the Visiting Committee reported in 1918 that "many girls are in one dormitory with no privacy at all," with twenty-five girls to one toilet, bathtub, and lavatory. The report stressed that "in order to secure the higher type of student nurse, the girl of superior education, high ideals, and morals above reproach, and to retain such after graduation, it is most essential that the whole environment of the girl in training be improved, and put upon the highest possible plane."[19]

Housing was greatly helped with the completion of the Harkness Nurses' Home in 1932. Two other large off-campus residences became available for nurses: the John Waterhouse residence in Makiki, given to Queen's in 1941 by Theo. H.

Davies & Co., Ltd., housing thirty to forty nurses; and Ahi-puʻu, the Nuʻuanu Valley estate of Mr. and Mrs. George Sherman on temporary loan from their daughter Mrs. Laura N. Dowsett, housing sixty nurses beginning in 1947.

Applicants to the School of Nursing were to be in good health and provide a certificate from a responsible person as to their moral character. Student nurses were required to stand when a doctor entered the room, even if they were busy at work. Dr. James Stewart recalled that when he first came to Queen's in the early 1960s, this was still done, although the practice was already fading on the mainland. The head nurse would say, "The doctor's here—stand up."[20] Students were also expected to give up their chairs to doctors. If a student didn't show these gestures of respect, she would be reported to the director of nursing and be reprimanded. Students were also expected to behave in an upright manner when off duty. There was a 10 P.M. curfew at nurses' quarters. Freshmen usually lived on the first floor, said Nancy Kim, who periodically heard knocking on her window from an upper-class student who wanted to sneak back to her room past curfew. The school also wanted their

nurses to be well rounded. They were required to attend chapel, and had to be able to swim the length of the pool at the Harkness Nurses' Home.

In the beginning, only an eighth grade education was required for admission, as nursing was mostly a hands-on occupation (although "women of superior educational advantages" were given preference). As theory and science played larger roles, more education was required. By 1929, the prerequisite for admission was a high school diploma. By 1932, students were further required to complete a year's work at the University of Hawaiʻi prior to entrance. In the 1940s, students were required to pass the National League for Nursing Qualifying Exam. (A minimum height of five feet and proportionate weight was also required.) During World War II, one year of prenursing courses at the University of Hawaiʻi was added. The program now included forty practical and theoretical courses in the classroom, plus carefully supervised ward practice. In the beginning, just a few physicians gave lectures; now nineteen loaned their expertise. In the 1950s, the high school diploma requirement came with conditions: the prospective student was to have completed coursework in geometry, biology, chemistry, and two years of a foreign language. The applicant also had to meet the minimum entrance requirements for the University of Hawai'i.

Enrollment continued to increase, and an extra class was added in 1941. However, a collegiate school of nursing was established at the University of Hawai'i in 1951 by the territorial legislature. The move was in line with a national trend in nurses' training, which was beginning to shift to universities, and signaled the beginning of the end for most hospital-based nursing schools in America. The Queen's Hospital School of Nursing continued to be strong, however, and by 1959 had issued over nine hundred diplomas. In competitive examinations, Queen's graduates ranked in the upper 10 percent nationally.

By the late 1960s, it was becoming obvious that the school could not provide what young women—and men—needed to advance their careers: a degree from an accredited university. The board of directors saw that this was in keeping with the times, and so, after fifty-two years of providing nursing education, The Queen's Hospital School of Nursing graduated its last class with thirty-five students in 1968 and closed its doors.

opposite
Queen's nurses' choir, 1937.

below
The Queen's Hospital School of Nursing's last graduating class—the class of 1968.

Nurse Evelyn Balenzuela pours tea for her patient from a thermos type jug provided by funds donated by Queen's employees in 1955. Improvements to patient comfort that year also included "hot pack" meals, which were delivered still sizzling even to rooms far away from the kitchen.

A NEW STANDARD OF CARE

1950–Present

By the 1950s, many fearful diseases that ran rampant through the population were under control. In 1956, Dr. Nils Larsen reported that infant mortality had dropped to a new low.[1] By 1958, forty-four years had elapsed without a single case of smallpox in Hawaiʻi. Eleven years had passed without a death from typhoid fever. Diphtheria and tetanus were all but eliminated. In contrast to epidemic-level polio in Hawaiʻi in the 1940s and early 1950s, the Salk polio vaccine of 1954 cut the number to forty-six reported cases by 1956. While there were 6.7 per 100,000 tuberculosis cases in 1956, the rate was cut to 3.1 in 1958.[2] Despite these remarkable successes, other diseases were on the rise. Larsen cited a rising cancer rate and unprecedented high blood pressure and strokes.[3] In the 1980s, unforeseen diseases such as HIV/AIDS would appear in epidemic proportions. The Queen's Hospital needed to grow and expand, not only with new infrastructure but also with advances in medicine.

A New Era of Growth

In 1953, both hospital staff and the general public saw a need to expand The Queen's Hospital. The importance of a well-equipped hospital now extended beyond the borders of Hawaiʻi, as Queen's was now known as the "medical center of the Pacific." The June 1953 issue of the *Paradise of the Pacific* stated, "Today The Queen's Hospital is in the midst of a drive to raise funds to build a wing, critically needed to relieve congestion, overcrowding and other conditions impinging upon its efficient services, not only to . . . Oahu, but to all the islands of the Hawaiian chain, to other islands of the Pacific and to ships making port on occasion."

The Queen's Hospital secured federal grants totaling $383,000 for the new wing. There was also a hospital building fund of $200,000, and, as of June 1953, donations totaled $201,000.[4] A radio campaign garnered more donations toward the cost of the building, which was approximately $1,329,000[5] (about $8.9 million in 2008 dollars).[6] Hawaiʻi

architect Vladimir Ossipoff designed the four-story, 55-by-271-foot building, which was called the Kamehameha IV Wing (later just the Kamehameha Wing), to honor Alexander Liholiho. It was built at the end of Kīnaʻu, perpendicular to it and running back toward Punchbowl Crater. There were now six major wings at The Queen's Hospital. At the front, from left to right, was Pauahi (1904), Nalani (1924), and Kīnaʻu (1945). Behind these wings at right angles to them were Bishop (1893), Liholiho (1925), and Kamehameha (1954).

The Kamehameha Wing was dedicated on October 13, 1954. An elaborate pageant, written and directed by Dr. Larsen, drew an overflow crowd. Actors played King Kamehameha IV and Queen Emma, and Dr. Charles Judd Jr., great-grandson of Dr. Gerrit P. Judd, portrayed the missionary surgeon. The pageant traced the history of medicine in the islands from the arrival of the Polynesians through the Chinese and Japanese immigration waves. Dances of each nation were represented, complete with ethnic costumes, including over thirty kimono-clad women. The children of doctors and hospital staff marched on stage with the flags of fifty-seven nations.[7]

The Kamehameha Wing added a total of 106 new beds, but replaced fifty-seven unacceptable ones in the aging Pauahi Wing for a net gain of forty-nine and a total bed count of 404. The fourth floor of the surgical wing housed eleven operating rooms, each with a separate transformer on the roof to warn of defective equipment. The floors featured terrazzo carbon black over grounded metal wire to make them nonconductive[8]—a safety feature to protect against the hazards of static electricity and the newer anesthetic gases. Modern surgery lights were also installed—at a cost of $1,200 each; none of the operating rooms had windows.[9] One of the surgical suites featured a "Television Eye" that could transmit surgeries to the first floor Kamehameha Auditorium for nurse and intern training. Techniques could now be observed by many students instead of only the half-dozen who could

Aerial view from January 1985 showing the construction of the Queen Emma Tower behind the Nalani and Kīna'u wings.

The new Kamehameha Wing designed by Vladimir Ossipoff and constructed in 1954.

opposite page, clockwise from top left
Queen's staff move into the new Kamehameha Wing, 1955.

The Kamehameha 3 surgical floor featured private rooms equipped with an electric bed, TV, phone, and intercom.

Vladimir Ossipoff's architectural rendering of the entrance to the Kamehameha wing.

VAIKIKI ENTRANCE
QUEEN'S HOSPITAL ·· NEW SURGERY WING
VLADIMIR OSSIPOFF · ARCHITECT

stand in a typical operating room. Patients were constantly monitored in fourteen postoperative beds until they recovered sufficiently to be transferred back to their rooms. The cost for the "ultramodern" surgical floor was $500,000.

The second level offered semiprivate and private rooms, along with a complete pediatric unit and isolation facilities. On the third level, there were semiprivate rooms and private rooms for the "well-to-do," furnished with bedside TVs and toasters. Electric beds made their first appearance at Queen's in Kamehameha.[10] The days when a patient had to call a nurse to crank a bed to a different position were rapidly fading.

The completion of the Kamehameha Wing allowed patients to be moved from the Pauahi and Bishop wings. The overcrowded Out-Patient Department tripled its floor space to 12,000 square feet by moving to the vacated Pauahi. Pediatrics also relocated to Kamehameha 2. Although the other Kamehameha units were up and running by November 1954, the surgery unit didn't open until January 29, 1955, when the entire unit was transferred from Nalani 4. The first operation in the new surgery unit, an emergency tracheotomy, was performed at noon that day. As the hospital grew, the Kamehameha Wing took on many other purposes, but is still in use today.

A NEW STANDARD OF CARE

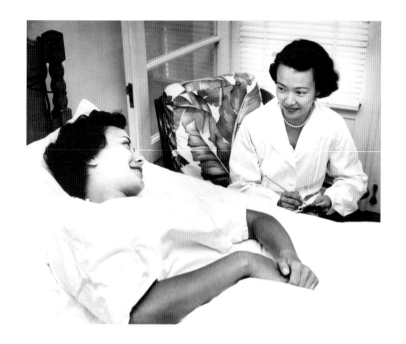
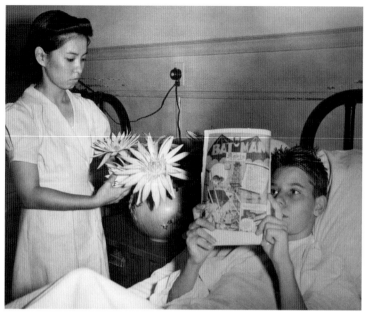

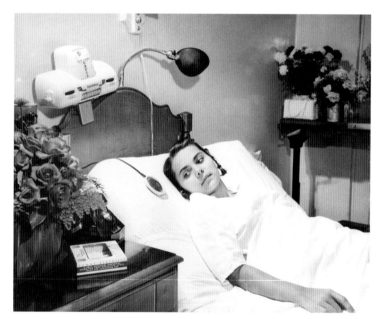

Clockwise from top left:

Nobuko Kaneda Mookini, MSW, of Social Services
with a patient in 1955.

A nurse arranges flowers for a pediatric patient,
circa late 1950s.

Queen's first intercom system for patients. A large, white
radio was also clipped to the headboard, circa 1950s.

Martha Werick of Occupational Therapy teaches
nature crafts, 1956.

Technicians perform hematology tests at the laboratory
on Bishop 4, 1956.

Myrtle Lee dances the hula in the Nalani Wing lobby during
Aloha Week, 1956.

Mrs. Trainovitch gives a Hospital Day tour of the Nalani Wing, circa 1950s.

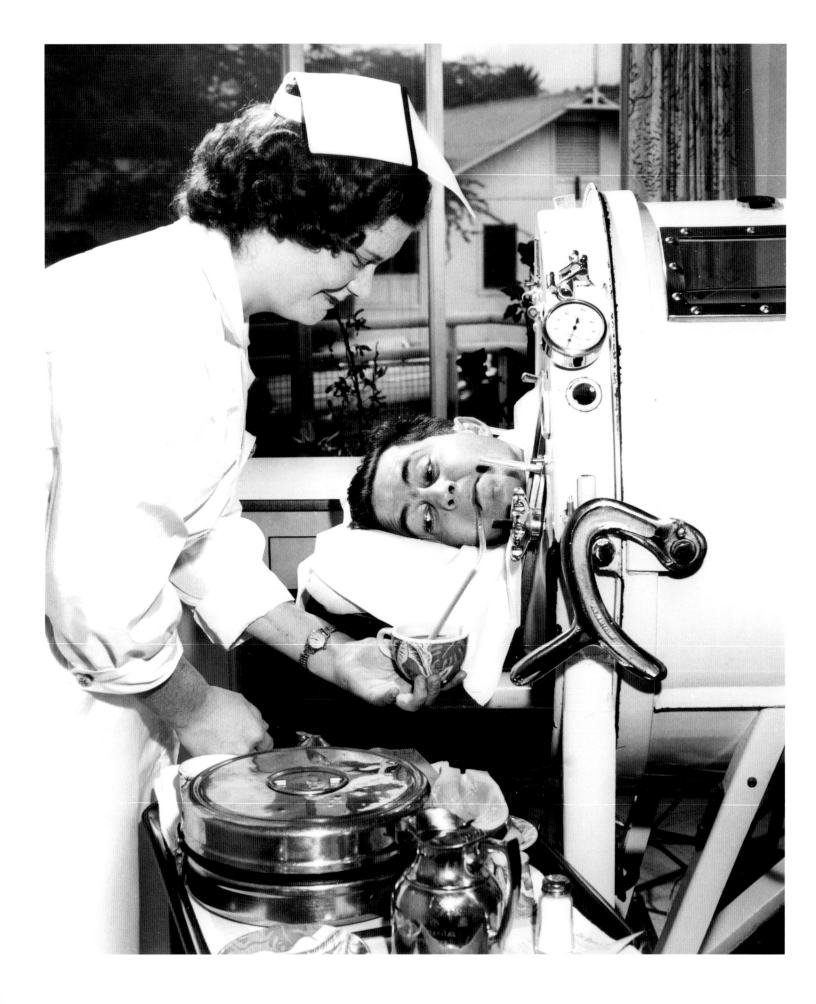

On the blackboard:

Formula Making–Terminal Method
To keep nipples from plugging:
1. Place bottle caps on loosely.
2. Keep water level below milk level.
3. Boil for 25 minutes only.
4. Cool to room temperature.
5. Shake bottles gently before placing in refrigerator.

An Out-Patient Department (now known as the Queen Emma Clinics) formula-making class in 1953.

opposite
Newspaper columnist Bob Krauss demonstrates an iron lung at Queen's for the March of Dimes, 1957. Krauss wrote for the *Honolulu Advertiser* for fifty-five years, from 1951 through 2006.

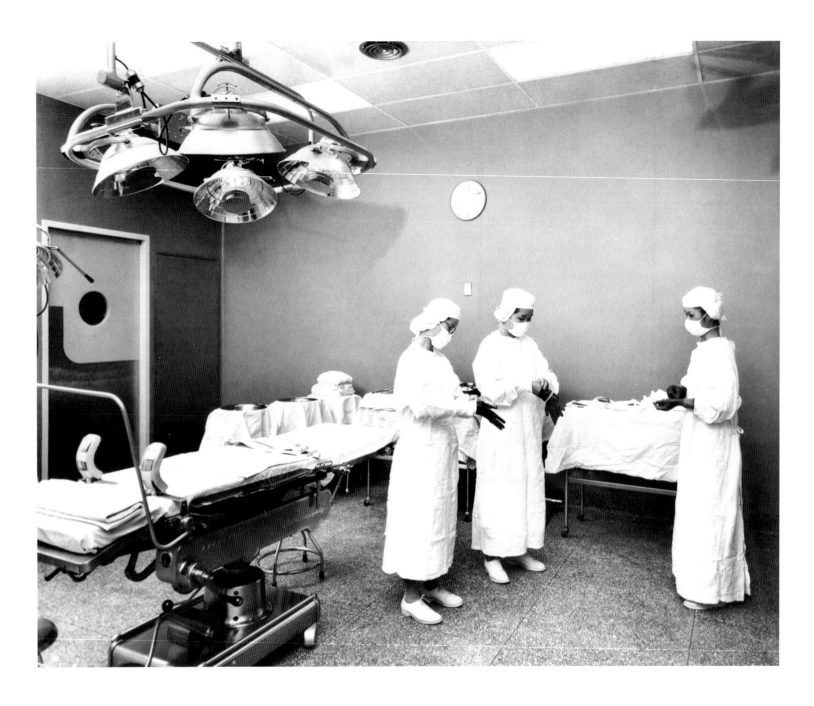

Nurses in a Queen's operating room, circa 1950s.

Surgery—Minimizing Pain to Minimally Invasive

The only doctor at The Queen's Hospital in the early days, Dr. William Hillebrand was also a skilled surgeon, as suggested by this newspaper announcement (translated from Hawaiian):

NOSE! NOSE!! Who doesn't have a nose and desires one? Check out the nose of the Chinese man that Dr. Hillebrand attached, and purchase one for yourself. If you lack a nose, this doctor can make one for you.[11]

There is no known photo, however, of the patient after the surgery. In the days before anesthesia, a good surgeon had to be quick to minimize the pain. The discovery of anesthetics allowed surgeons to go deeper into the body and perform longer operations. Basic surgical techniques began to improve. Antisepsis and asepsis helped control infection, and the discovery of antibiotics significantly increased patient safety. Anesthetics steadily improved too. In 1906, Dr. A. W. Morton of San Francisco visited Queen's to demonstrate the first use of spinal anesthesia in Hawai'i. Using cocaine dissolved in cerebro-spinal fluid, he injected the anesthetic into the subarachnoid space where spinal fluid circulates. With twenty-five physicians present in the then new Pauahi operating room, Morton successfully demonstrated the repair of a hernia, followed by the treatment of a sixty-five-year-old man suffering from osteomyelitis of the femur with involvement of the knee joint. He believed spinal anesthesia was superior to ether and chloroform, which sometimes caused complications and deaths in healthy patients.[12] Morton used spinal anesthesia for surgeries on all parts of the body, from the amputation of a toe to trephining (drilling a hole in the head).[13]

In 1911, the hospital saw 588 surgeries. By 1920, the number jumped to 2,068. With the completion of the Queen Emma Building (Nalani) and the Liholiho Wing in 1925, Queen's boasted two large and two small operating rooms. By 1951, 5,832 surgeries were done at Queen's; it was not uncommon for thirty operations to occur in a single day. In 1977, surgeries topped 20,000 a year, and in 2009, with seventeen operating rooms, over 23,000 were performed.

In 1977, a severed thumb was saved by a Queen's surgeon using microsurgery, the first digit reattachment in Hawai'i.

Specially designed microscopes made it possible to connect successively smaller blood vessels and nerves, typically one millimeter in diameter. A microsurgery training program was launched in 1980. Laparoscopic, or minimally invasive surgery (MIS), came into use with the development of the computer chip television camera in 1985. With a magnified view of the surgical area viewable on a monitor, MIS surgeons operate by inserting a thin, lighted viewing lens (the laparoscope) and tiny surgical instruments through small incisions. The advantages of MIS are smaller incisions, better cosmetics, quicker recovery, and decreased wound complications.[14] MIS procedures are performed in numerous types of surgeries, and the list continues to grow.[15] In 2004, two operating rooms were redesigned and telemedicine technology was installed for an MIS teaching and training center. MIS procedures could also be viewed remotely at a surgical skills training facility in a separate area, with training equipment for surgeons.

If MIS represents a trend in health care, then robotic surgery is a trend in MIS. In 2007, Queen's purchased its first surgical "robot." Although standard for many surgeries, MIS had not been widely used for complex or delicate procedures because fine manipulation of the rigid, hand-held laparoscopic instruments is difficult.[16] With robotic technology, surgeons can use MIS techniques in delicate procedures like prostatectomies and heart valve repair. Miniature surgical instruments are attached to four robotic arms, giving the surgeon an extra pair of hands. Although called robotic, the equipment is completely controlled by the surgeon at a remote unit using intuitive hand controls. The surgeon can easily switch control from one arm to another. For example, two arms can be used to tie a suture, while a third wields miniature shears and the fourth positions the camera.[17]

In 2008, Single Incision Laparoscopic Surgery (SILS) was introduced at Queen's, taking certain MIS procedures a step further. While most MIS procedures use four small incisions, SILS uses just one half-inch incision. The first SILS surgery was a gallbladder removal, done through the patient's belly button. SILS cuts recovery time from five to six weeks to one to two weeks after a short hospital stay.

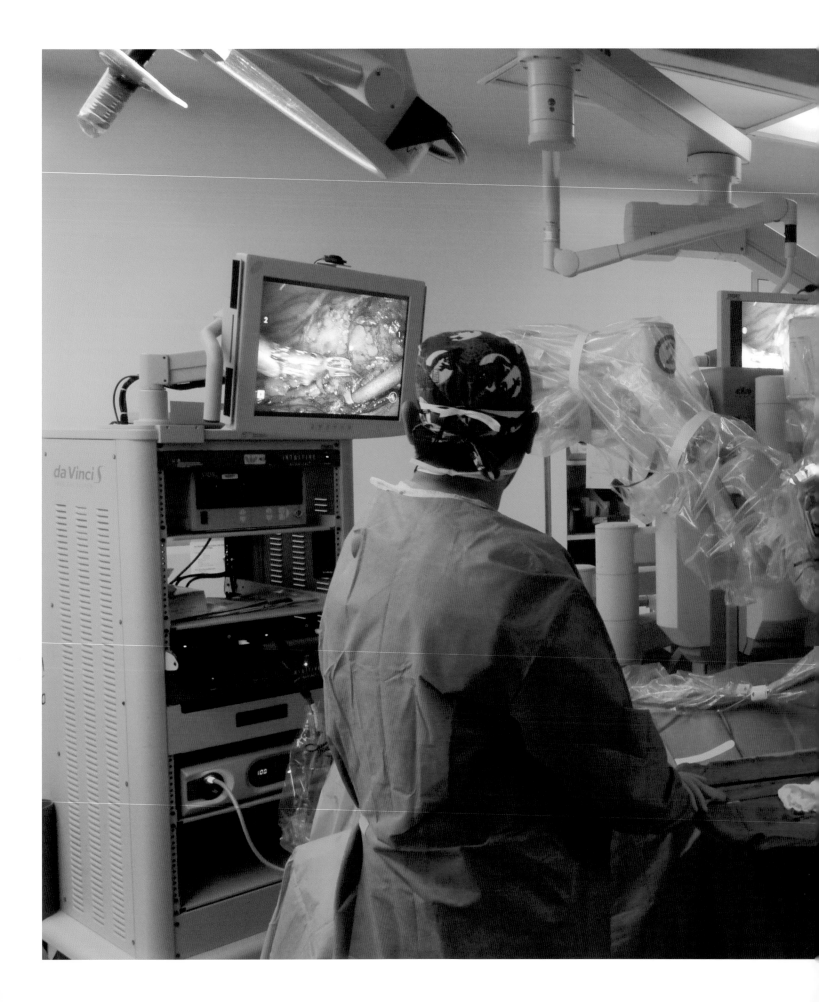

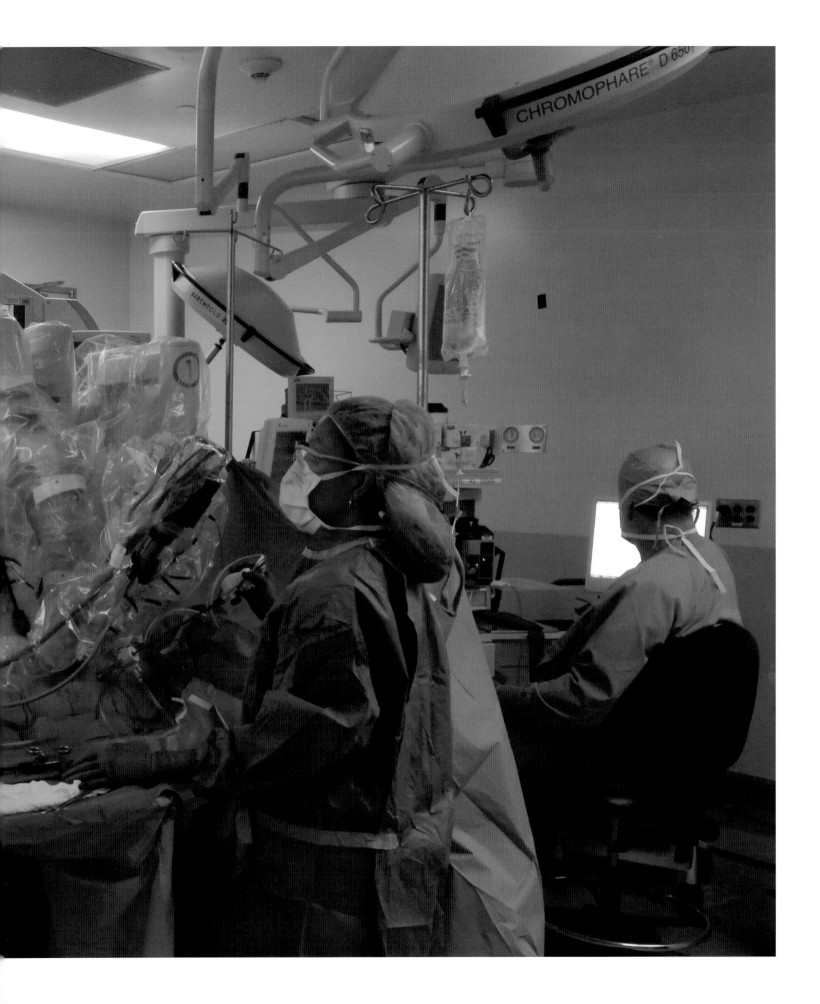

The first open heart surgery in Hawai'i, performed in 1959, involved sixty-five people, from housekeepers to surgeons. About two-thirds of them were present for a group photo.

previous page
The da Vinci robotic surgery system is used to perform a minimally invasive pyeloplasty (an operation to correct a blockage between the kidney and the ureter) surgical procedure. The green lighting eliminates glare from the monitors, which are used exclusively for the procedure. *Left to right*: Norbert Dolor, surgical technologist; Eliza Ilano, RN; and Greg Wilson, MD, anesthesiologist. The surgeon (not pictured), urologist Sergei Tikhonenkov, MD, controls the surgical robot from a remote unit.

First Open Heart Surgery in Hawai'i

The Queen's Hospital celebrated its 100th anniversary on August 1, 1959, three weeks before Hawai'i's statehood on August 21. The only hospital in the United States established by royalty, Queen's had existed during the days of the Hawaiian Kingdom, the Republic of Hawai'i, the Territory of Hawai'i, and now the State of Hawai'i. During the first election after statehood, absentee ballots were passed out to registered voters who were patients at Queen's.[18]

Early in the morning of December 2, 1959, Queen's was preparing for an event that would be either a landmark or a disaster. The first open heart surgery in Hawai'i would be performed in the new Kamehameha surgical wing. "It was considered a huge risk," said Dr. Albert Chun, one of the surgeons.[19] A mother of two young children, the patient was a thirty-six-year-old Hilo housewife with two holes in her heart, a serious congenital defect that would lead to a premature death. Surgeons would have to stop her heart for thirty minutes while they sutured the holes shut.

Key to the complex surgery was the heart-lung machine, which circulates blood while the patient's heart is stopped by taking oxygen-depleted blood out, reoxygenating it, and returning it to the body. Heart-lung machine technology was still very new in 1959, and many prominent programs on the mainland had started out with fatalities. Queen's first heart-lung machine was partially custom built by the open heart surgical team. The surgery was backed by two years of preparation, which involved the training of staff, fine-tuning of equipment, and experimentation. Beginning in 1956, lead surgeon Dr. Scott C. Brainard and team began experimental heart surgeries on dogs in the old obstetrics delivery rooms. When the team required more space, they were given a World War II orderly barracks and kitchen at the *mauka* (mountain) end of the Kamehameha Wing. Part of the barracks was used for dog kennels, which resulted in frequent early morning calls from the nursing supervisor complaining that the racket was disturbing patients. The kitchen was set up for surgery.[20] A large number of animals were required each week. The Hawaiian Humane Society was reluctant to be involved, but eventually allowed the heart team to anesthetize dogs that were going to be put to sleep anyway to obtain blood to prime the heart-lung machine. Since the Humane Society was not willing to provide animals for surgery, members of the house staff and friends would purchase the largest dogs available each week.[21] Many dogs were also donated.

The surgical team did an open heart surgery on a dog every Wednesday morning. The right ventricle of the heart was opened for a minimum of thirty minutes, then closed, and the dog was watched for survival. The considerable amount of electrical equipment often caused a fuse to blow. Someone would have to replace the fuse during the operation, and one item would be hand-powered to prevent blowing another. By November 1959, the team had performed one hundred open heart procedures on dogs and felt ready to operate on a human. In anticipation of the first human surgery, additional electrical circuits were added to one of the oper-

ating rooms. Two more dog operations were conducted to make sure the equipment, which had been transferred to the operating room, was working properly.

There were fourteen people on the open heart surgical team. Four surgeons performed the operation. Assisting chief surgeon Scott Brainard were Drs. Noboru Akagi, Albert Chun, and Carl Mason. Dr. Paul Gebauer operated the heart-lung machine. Blood temperature, rate of flow, pressure, and volume were monitored by Dr. Unoji Goto. Dr. John Hanley and anesthetist Thelma Jones administered the anesthesia and monitored the patient's condition minute by minute. The others on the team were laboratory technician Mary Connor, who processed and prepared the blood of fifteen donors to prime the heart-lung machine and for transfusion during surgery; electronics technician Bill Kekoa; scrub nurses Frances Batura and Mabel Oshiro; and circulating nurses Edythe Yoshihara and Marian Endo.

The patient's life rode on the success of the surgery. Dr. Brainard opined twenty years later that if it had been a failure, the community would have been discouraged and lost confidence in open heart surgery. The surgical team closed the two holes, and the thirty-six-year-old mother's heart was completely repaired. After a three-week recovery at the hospital, she returned home. The team went on to perform over twenty successful operations. In 1965, Dr. Gebauer fabricated a heat exchanger (which cooled the blood to lower the patient's body temperature) out of hydraulic airplane tubing. His heat exchanger fit into the oxygenator, allowing oxygenation and cooling at the same time, thereby reducing trauma to the blood. Gebauer's invention was manufactured by a surgical equipment company for use in other hospitals.

In 2008, the patient, now eighty-five, visited Queen's. Two of the original surgeons, Drs. Akagi and Chun, were there to greet her. Circulating nurse Edythe Yoshihara also came. Dr. Scott Brainard joined the reunion by speakerphone from his home in Oregon. "My heart is good," said the former patient, who had outlived all but three of the seven doctors on the surgical team. Two years after the surgery, her husband passed away. She said that her life had been hard because she had to raise her children by herself. "But they came out alright," she reflected. "[Without the surgery] I wouldn't have been around to raise them."[22]

Healing Hearts—From the Electrocardiograph to Queen's Heart

The Queen's Hospital's first electrocardiograph (EKG) apparatus was purchased in 1936. Cardiac catheterization—the insertion of a catheter into a chamber of the heart for diagnostic and interventional purposes—followed the 1959 open heart surgery. In 1968, a five-bed coronary care unit was opened, and starting in 1971, physical and occupational therapy were included in coronary rehabilitation, representing the first cardiac rehab program in Hawai'i. Two years later, an eleven-bed cardiac surgery unit opened. By 1978, 1,354 open heart surgeries had been performed. The Queen Emma Tower, built in 1985, included a new cardiac catheterization lab, two operating rooms dedicated to open heart surgery, a cardiac intensive care unit, and a heart monitoring unit. In 2003, Queen's established the forty-bed Cardiac Comprehensive Care Unit on Queen Emma Tower 6. Here, cardiac patients at all levels can be cared for in adaptable rooms, from telemetry (heart monitoring) to critical care.

In a move to unify cardiac care, all heart-related services are now known as Queen's Heart; its practitioners say that Queen's Heart is located anywhere cardiac patients are treated. In 2007, Queen's joined a national program to systematically transport heart attack patients from the emergency room to a catheterization lab for balloon angioplasty in ninety minutes or less to restore blood flow, dramatically increasing survival and minimizing heart muscle damage. To further speed treatment, Queen's equipped twenty city and county ambulances with portable EKG equipment, which

Open heart surgery at Queen's, 1978.

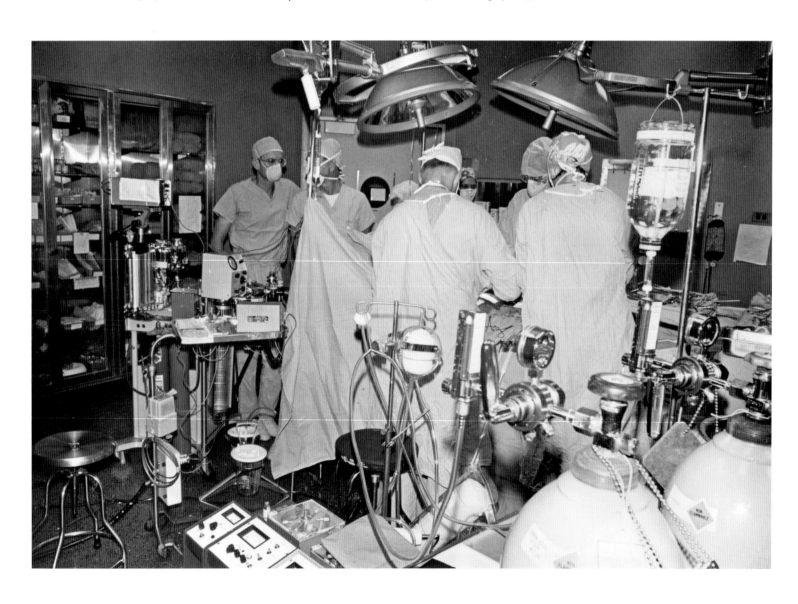

wirelessly notifies Queen's of a heart attack in sixteen seconds, providing up to an extra twenty minutes to prepare for the incoming patient.[23] Queen's Heart has also made efforts to address cardiac care statewide, especially in remote areas. A Cardiac Transfer Center was established to guarantee beds to patients who require specialized treatment at Queen's.

The Changing Face of Queen's

In 1958, construction began on new facilities, but complete changes to the look of the entire hospital were planned. Designed by architect Vladimir Ossipoff, the $4.5 million project (about $26.9 million in 2008 dollars)[24] had three major parts. The first was a new five-story wing (four levels, plus a ground floor). The name 'Iolani was chosen unanimously for the new wing by the board and has a historic connection to Queen's—Alexander Liholiho 'Iolani was the founder of the hospital. 'Iolani was suggested by Mary Kawena Pukui and connotes the soaring Hawaiian hawk. The *'io* is prominent in Hawaiian mythology and one of only two extant birds of prey native to the islands; "*lani*" means "heaven" or "sky."

The 'Iolani Wing changed the familiar face of Queen's, which had existed since 1924. Rather than follow the straight line of buildings in front, 'Iolani jutted forward from the right side of Nalani, replacing about a quarter of its façade. Ossipoff brought his version of midcentury modernism to many buildings in Hawai'i, including the Honolulu International Airport terminals, the University of Hawai'i Administration Building, and the Hawai'i Medical Library at Queen's. His style reflected functionality and economy of design in a tropical setting.

The first floor of the 'Iolani Wing became the new emergency room, which migrated a short distance from its former location in Nalani. The Nalani emergency room had space for only four patients; the new one accommodated eleven, and ambulances could now back up at the proper height for patient delivery. Employee Health, Information Services, and Human Resources were located here also, as well as Rusty's Hairstyling and Barber Shop for men and women, which offered services in patient rooms. On the second level were thirty beds—two private and fourteen semiprivate rooms— for medical and surgical patients. Obstetrical patients and the nursery were on the third level, with twenty-three beds

The Ossipoff-designed Nalani entrance and lobby (left) and 'Iolani Wing (right) were completed in 1960. The pink bombax tree, planted by Dr. William Hillebrand, sheds all its leaves before blooming between January and May.

in private, semiprivate, and triple rooms, many with adjoining verandas. Wards of four to six beds were becoming a thing of the past for new mothers at the hospital. Four nurseries with plate glass windows accommodated forty-two infants. The new maternity area adjoined the older one on Nalani 3. The pathology laboratory was located on the fourth level, where it remains today, and animal labs were kept on the fifth. The hospital's capacity rose to 425 beds.

The antiseptic white and putty color typical of hospitals disappeared with the 'Iolani Wing in favor of chocolate, eggshell, blue-green, mustard, and other fashionable pastels of the time. Improvements brought patient rooms closer to what is considered standard today. The 'Iolani Wing featured electric push-button beds with built-in radios, and nightstands with Swedish style upright telephones. Closeness to

Pharmacist Irene Chai fills a prescription in the new Nalani pharmacy, 1960.

below
The new 'Iolani Wing Emergency Department, 1960. Staff nurse Ann Edmunds (left), treats a patient in one of four examining rooms, while the orderly Lloyd Tobera (center) and staff nurse Barbara Ideta retrieve supplies from a work area.

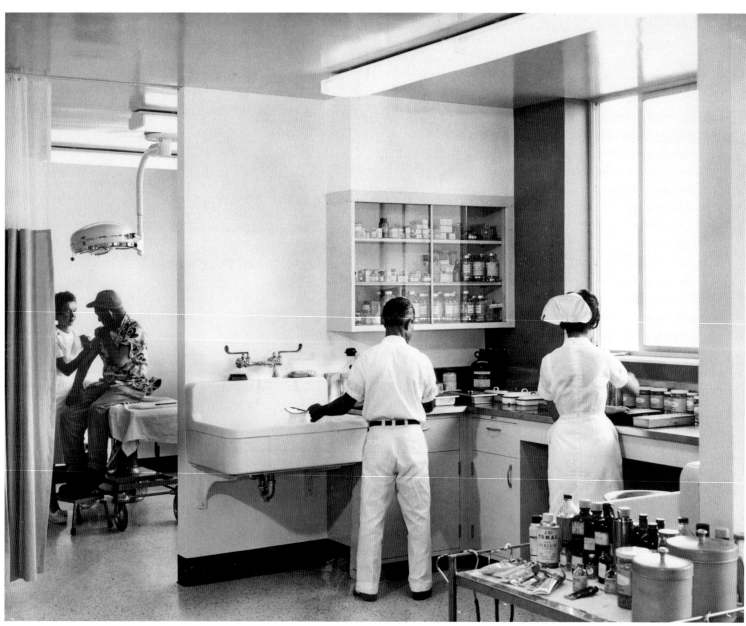

Queen's staff prepare food for patients in the dietary kitchen, 1960. *Clockwise from front left*: Elsie Miyahira, therapeutic dietitian; Bernice Hamada, kitchen helper; Dionicio Bautista, porter; Gavino Doronio, dishwasher; and Fred Capinia, pantryman.

the outdoors was still considered good for patients, so large screened windows admitted sunshine and fresh air.[25]

The second part of the project was a two-story extension in front of Nalani, creating a more spacious lobby with a new coffee shop, gift shop, and pharmacy, with business offices above. The Nalani Wing was now recessed from the new front of the hospital, although its upper floors could still be seen. The aging Pauahi Wing to the left of Nalani was torn down for the third part of the project: a new two-story Pauahi Wing housing Queen's School of Nursing classrooms and the Out-Patient Department. Connected to the lobby area, the new Pauahi would remain a two-story structure until plans to add six additional stories were realized in 1971.

Nurses and visitors enjoy a break in the new coffee shop off of the main lobby, 1960.

opposite
Queen's entrance and lobby, 1971.

The entire project was dedicated on July 16, 1960, a day shy of the 100th anniversary of the laying of the original cornerstone. The ceremony was patterned after the 1860 one; the king's cornerstone speech was read to the audience. The Royal Hawaiian Band was on hand, and The Queen's Hospital Student Nurse Chorus sang "Aloha Oe" and Queen Emma's song, "Kaleleonalani." In 1960, The Queen's Hospital needed slightly over two employees for each patient to maintain round-the-clock services. The trend in modern medicine required the talents of more and more professionals. Among them were doctors, registered nurses, X-ray technicians, laboratory technicians, occupational and physical therapists, radiologists, and others with specialized training. Queen's now employed over 670 people. Hospital expenses continued to increase as new diagnosis and treatment methods called for expensive new drugs and complex equipment—and the highly trained personnel who came with them.

Cancer Treatment at Queen's

The oldest surviving records of cancer cases at The Queen's Hospital are found in an 1878 report, although there were most certainly earlier cases. Treatment consisted only of surgery, although doctors recognized from the earliest times that cancer usually recurred. The use of radiation to shrink tumors dates to the early twentieth century, and some success was achieved with chemotherapy drugs, which were first developed in the 1940s. Today, a combination of surgery, chemotherapy, and radiation is used in many cases.

In the 1920s, the territorial legislature appropriated $30,000 to buy radium for use in cancer therapy, and in 1931, a Queen's cancer clinic was established for outpatients. A Deep Roentgen Therapy machine was installed in 1942, and Queen's established the first tumor board in 1949. In 1960, cancer therapy got a boost with a two million volt X-ray machine installed in the new Pauahi Out-Patient Department. Designed to treat deep-seated tumors, the machine was a vast improvement over older equipment with less power. Patients experienced less skin reaction and complained of fewer ills, and the average treatment time was three minutes, as compared to fifteen, with ten patients treated per day.

A cancer registry, tumor clinic, and chemotherapy research were established to support better treatment outcomes, followed by the first oncology unit in Hawai'i, which was established in 1970 within Queen's Department of Surgery. Cancer treatment began to coalesce with a comprehensive cancer care program established at Queen's in 1976, and an oncology unit opened on Nalani 3 the following year. In 1972, Queen's was given custodial control of the state's supply of radium, and in the same year acquired its first linear accelerator, which had just become commercially available.

Linear accelerators use electromagnetic fields to propel subatomic particles to great speeds, then smashes them into a heavy metal to produce X-rays that shrink tumors.

By the late 1970s, radiation therapy as a cancer treatment had grown such that a dedicated building was required. The Blood Bank had moved out, so its building at Queen's was razed to build Nā'ea Radiation Therapy, completed in 1979. The building is named after the *ali'i* George Nā'ea, Queen Emma's natural father. Unlike other buildings at Queen's, Nā'ea is built mostly below ground to contain radiation. Above ground is a cement bunkerlike protrusion with landscaping on top, small windows, and a skylight. When Nā'ea opened, about fifty patients were treated daily; today, over 120 patients are treated.

The goal of radiation therapy is to focus radiation on tumors with as little damage to healthy tissue as possible. In the past, radiation therapy technicians used X-rays to identify the location of tumors by approximating the position of organs in relation to the skeletal structure. In 1997, Queen's acquired a treatment planning system that uses CT technology to create three-dimensional images of tumors and surrounding tissue, greatly enhancing the accuracy of delivery.[26] New technology delivers more radiation to tumors and less to healthy tissue by varying the amount of radiation to different parts of the treatment area. Another radiation technology called stereotactic radio surgery precisely focuses radiation to perform highly complex neurosurgical procedures, accurate to within a half millimeter. Recent technology includes TomoTherapy, a CT scanner-based device that uses image guided, helical radiation delivery to target tumors more accurately for certain types of cases.

In 1991, a forty-eight-bed unit (including six beds for bone marrow transplant patients) was created on Queen Emma Tower 7. Radioactive seed implant treatment, begun in 1998, made Queen's the first in Hawai'i to offer a complete range of prostate cancer therapies. The most recent development in cancer care was the establishment of the Queen's Cancer Center in 2007. Housed in a remodeled Kīna'u 1, the $6 million center brings together almost every aspect of cancer diagnosis and treatment, minimizing the need for multiple visits to scattered medical services. A patient navigator assists patients through the entire treatment process.[27]

The Queen's Medical Center, circa 1975. *Left to right*: Pauahi Wing (1971), Nalani Wing (1924), and 'Iolani Wing (1960).

left The kapok tree dominated Queen's front lawn in 1978, as it did in earlier decades. Directly behind the tree is the coffee shop; to the right is the entrance to the lobby.

opposite
A Pauahi Wing semi-private room with a view of Punchbowl Street below, 1971.

The High-Rise Hospital

Architect Vladimir Ossipoff was brought in to finish what he had begun in 1960. The new, $5.5 million (about $23.4 million in 2008 dollars)[28] Pauahi addition, dedicated on May 23, 1971, totaled eight stories (seven numbered levels, plus a ground level). The bulk of the financing came from Queen Emma estate earnings. The federal Hill-Burton Act provided $680,000, and the state contributed $400,000.[29] Although 202 urgently needed beds were added, the bed count increased by just thirty-three for a total of 480, because six- and ten-bed wards in older wings were closed and used for other purposes.[30] At this time, chilled water equipment was installed to air condition the whole hospital.

The new Pauahi was the first wing with no wards. The only wards left at Queen's were nine three-bed orthopedic units for patients requiring minimal care. Pauahi's floors were designed with double corridors. Equipment, service facilities, and the nursing station were in the center of each floor between the corridors, and patient rooms were on the outer perimeter. The six new floors offered ninety semi-private and twenty-two private rooms. Each floor featured wall-to-wall carpeting, hardwood paneling, sound-reducing acoustical ceiling tiles, and colorful drapery. Oxygen and compressed air were available at each bedside unit, and a central vacuum system—the first in the state—reduced noise and dust. Other conveniences included patient consoles with

Hawai'i Medical Library

The Hawai'i Medical Library began in two rooms of a bungalow on 'Iolani Palace grounds in 1913 with the donated collection of Dr. John S. McGrew, first president of the Hawai'i Medical Society. By 1916, the library moved to a room at The Queen's Hospital, and then due to lack of space, relocated to the Hawai'i Public Library in 1922. In only a year, the librarian began complaining about a lack of space. By 1934, the library had moved back to Queen's, this time to Liholiho 3. Finally, in 1941 it moved to what was thought to be a permanent home on the second floor of the Mabel Smyth Memorial Building. However, by 1959, a third of the collection was housed at Leahi Hospital. When the Queen's School of Nursing classes moved to the new Pauahi in 1960, the old nurses' school house was demolished to build the current Hawai'i Medical Library building, which opened in 1962.

phones and push-button controls for radio, TV, the nurse call system, draperies, and room light. In spite of the new wing, all beds at Queen's were occupied by July 1971. People on a waiting list were telephoned as patients were discharged. Administrators insisted, however, that Queen's could accommodate anyone requiring immediate hospitalization.[31] The Pauahi Wing is still a major patient care area, although the types of patients on the floors have changed over the years.

A One-Stop Medical Center

The Queen's Hospital's name was changed to The Queen's Medical Center in 1967[32] to reflect the broader scope of the institution. As six stories were being added to the Pauahi Wing, the board of directors and administrators already envisioned much more, and were proposing by 1970 to make Queen's a "one-stop medical center for medical, surgical, pediatric, obstetric and psychiatric care."[33] At the time, the average person visiting a doctor in Honolulu traveled to two or three locations for services such as X-rays, laboratory work, and filling prescriptions. Queen's concept was to have all services in one location.[34] The trustees' vision would be realized with the completion of a community mental health center, physicians' office building, parking garage, heliport, and a university medical instruction center.

In 1973, Queen's finished construction of its community mental health building, the first step in its transformation. The three-story building was named Kekela, after Queen Emma's natural mother, Fanny Kekelaokalani Young, the wife of high chief Nā'ea and the daughter of the Englishman John Young. The name Kekela means "opportunity." Awarded a construction grant from the National Institute of Mental Health, the $3 million Kekela, another Ossipoff design, became the largest inpatient psychiatric facility after the Hawai'i State Hospital. A comprehensive behavioral health care center with fifty-one beds, Kekela comprised a short-term acute care facility and an outpatient behavioral health clinic.[35] When the building was completed, patients were moved from Pu'uhonua to Kekela.

Behavioral health at Queen's developed into a continuum of services using outcome and evidence-based treatment. In 1998, Queen's began providing inpatient acute and residential behavioral health services for adolescents throughout the state. In 2002, outpatient behavioral health moved to a building on Vineyard Boulevard. The refurbished three-story structure was named Kaheiheimalie, after the grandmother of Kamehameha IV. "Kaheihei" is a contest, while "malie" means peaceful, gentle, or calm. Put together, the name suggests calm during a contest.

Excavation for the Physicians' Office Building (POB) and eight-hundred-car parking garage was well underway by 1974, and construction began the following year with Ossipoff continuing to be the principal designer. Opened in 1977, the POB (now called POB I) was situated on Lusitana Street behind the end of the Kamehameha Wing; Queen's patient care buildings had finally reached the topmost border of the property. The $13 million, ten-story building offered ninety offices for doctors. Even before the interior was completed, all the offices were spoken for by general practitioners, as well as by doctors in virtually every specialty. Today, 104 doctors practice in POB I. At street level was the POB I Pharmacy, where anyone could fill prescriptions. POB I is larger than it looks from the street. Below ground are three levels with laboratories, office space, utilities, and underground corridors that lead to the main Queen's buildings. Those who park in the POB I parking garage still access Queen's through these underground corridors, and staff can walk to Kekela or the University Tower without going outdoors.

The parking structure served a dual purpose. The $6 million, six-level structure (increased to eight levels and 1,046 stalls circa 1992) greatly expanded parking capacity and provided a place for medevac helicopters to land. The state legislature appropriated a major portion of the $400,000 price tag for the heliport, which became operational in 1978. Previously, the landing site had been the lawn of the State Capitol, which is adjacent to Queen's. Although it became a long-standing arrangement, the Capitol lawn landing site was meant to be temporary and had no markings, night lighting, wind direction indicators, or even a level landing surface.[36] Helicopters transporting emergency patients to the POB heliport were met by ambulances, which took them to the Queen's Emergency Room. The heliport (now called the helipad) was moved to the roof of the Queen Emma Tower when that building was completed in 1985.

The University of Hawai'i and The Queen's Medical Center collaborated to build the University Tower, the last phase of the project. The university obtained $27 million to pay for five new stories built on top of the three-story Kekela. In exchange, Queen's signed a twenty-five-year lease, dedicating the new floors to medical instruction conducted by the university's John A. Burns School of Medicine (JABSOM).

Build It and Doctors Will Come

The first Physicians' Office Building was filled almost instantly; office space for doctors at Queen's has been a coveted item since. Queen's had acquired property on the *mauka* (mountain) side of Lusitana Street almost in front of the POB I. An old realty building on the site served as mock-up rooms during the construction of the Queen Emma Tower, but the obvious best use of the site was a Physicians Office Building II and a new parking garage, both completed in 1991. POB II currently has sixty-four offices and 127 doctors, a second pharmacy open to the public, and a 770-stall parking garage.

Beginning in 2005, the former Honolulu Medical Group Building on the corner of Lauhala and Beretania streets underwent renovation and expansion. The building reopened in 2006 as the Physicians' Office Building III. Currently, the building has seventeen offices housing sixty-two doctors, a POB III Pharmacy, and a 250-stall parking garage. With the POB III, Queen's became the site of the largest concentration of physicians in the state.[37]

The Continuing Fight against Disease

In 1977, smallpox became the first disease completely eradicated by a vaccine, and after the introduction of penicillin, new antibiotics were discovered. Treatment for diabetes improved, and doctors at Queen's had a full library of heart medications available to them. Health consciousness got off the ground with cautions about cholesterol, and admonitions against smoking, which was eventually banned from hospital rooms, and then allowed nowhere on Queen's premises. However, the arrival of AIDS (acquired immunodeficiency syndrome) in Hawai'i in 1983 brought with it a fear of contagion reminiscent of earlier decades. Sets Yoshida, RN, was head nurse of the Kamehameha 2 infectious diseases ward when the epidemic began.[38] She remembers that everyone on her unit was required to use strict isolation procedures, and although her staff willingly faced the challenge, some temp agency nurses refused to work on the floor.

When the HIV (human immunodeficiency virus) was identified and better understood, infection control was relaxed, but precautions for needles and bodily fluids remained. More recently, antibiotic-resistant bacteria like MRSA (methicillin-resistant *Staphylococcus aureus*) became a danger to hospital patients, reinstating strict infection-control procedures.

The Future of Queen's

In 1982, The Queen's Medical Center was ready to embark on its most ambitious building project to date. An eleven-story tower (ten levels and a basement), which would cost $65 million (about $127.3 million in 2008 dollars),[39] represented "the future of Queen's," according to the medical center's president.[40] Originally referred to as the Liholiho Tower because it would replace the 1925 Liholiho Wing, the building became the Queen Emma Tower just before its completion in 1985.

Before the age of the high-rise hospital, it was easier to know where one was located in the complex of buildings, as the wings were at right angles with one another. That changed with the Queen Emma Tower, which was built right on the back of Nalani. All of the wings of The Queen's Medical Center are now connected in such a way that the older wings branch off from a hub on Nalani; at some points, one can walk from one building to the next without even noticing the change. At the Nalani hub, one can walk in one of several directions to either Pauahi, ʻIolani, Kīnaʻu (and then on to Kamehameha), or to the Queen Emma Tower.

The Queen Emma Tower (QET) has faceted edges in which balconies are placed, and at its core is a triangular open space. Windows in patient rooms along the outer walls look out over Honolulu, while rooms along the inner core look down on a garden. Not all the space was initially used, and floors remained unfinished until they were needed; the last two floors were built in 2003. The first level houses Imaging Services, with its X-ray, ultrasound, MRI, CT, and PET diagnostic machines. On the second level are core support services, such as Food and Nutrition Services, Central Processing and Distribution, and Central Transport Services. The surgical suites are placed on the third level, and in 2008, the new Queen's Heart catheterization labs were built on this floor. Levels 4 through 10 are patient floors, all private rooms with approximately forty beds per floor. On these levels are

medical and surgical ICUs, neuroscience ICU, Neuroscience Institute, cardiac, oncology, orthopedics, telemetry, and maternity. The new helipad on the roof of QET brought medevac patients only an elevator ride and a hallway away from the ER.

Branching Out

On February 1, 1987, Queen's extended its physical reach when Molokaʻi General Hospital (MGH) became a subsidiary of The Queen's Health Systems. Established by the Episcopal Church in 1932, MGH was known as Shingle Memorial Hospital until 1949, when it was incorporated as Molokaʻi Community Hospital. In 1963, the termite-ridden hospital was replaced by a new building financed with federal Hill-Burton and state funds. In 2005, Molokaʻi General Hospital completed an 11,193 square foot wing to provide updated services to patients. The partnership between Queen's and MGH has continued to make modern health care available to an isolated population of 7,500 residents.

Also in 1987, Queen's established the Queen's Health Care Centers, which brought primary care physicians and specialists to different parts of the state. A flagship Hawaiʻi Kai building was constructed in 2006. The 11,000 square foot facility brought comprehensive services to east Oʻahu, along with medical testing, imaging, and rehabilitation services.

Hawaiian Health for a New Millennium

Although many of the diseases that plagued Hawaiʻi in the early days have been conquered, there are major health disparities between Native Hawaiians and other groups. As a group, Hawaiians suffer disproportionately from hypertension, asthma, heart disease, and chronic lung disease. While the estimated incidence of diabetes was 3.1 percent in the United States in 2000, among native Hawaiians it was 22.42 percent and rising. Deaths from cancer and heart disease are also higher among native Hawaiians than other groups.

To address these issues, The Queen's Health Systems helped establish the Department of Native Hawaiian Health (DNHH) at the University of Hawaiʻi John A. Burns School of Medicine in 2002 by contributing $5 million over five years. The mission of the DNHH is to be an "academic center of excellence" to promote health and wellness to the Native Hawaiian community through research, education, and health care practices.[41] One goal was to form partnerships with native Hawaiian communities to develop effective models of health care. In 2005, the National Institutes of Health awarded a $6 million grant to The Queen's Medical Center and the DNHH to conduct four studies to reduce heart disease among native Hawaiians.

Focus on the health disparities was furthered by the establishment in 2008 of the Native Hawaiian Health Program (NHHP) at The Queen's Health Systems. The program endeavors to build health strategies for native Hawaiians into service lines at Queen's, beginning with Queen's Heart. The NHHP also sought research funding to align Queen's strengths with those most in need, and to increase access to Queen's services in the community.

Form and Function for a New Millennium

Large-scale construction from 1999 to 2004 of a new ER, Same Day Surgery Center, new parking garage, lobby, and Women's Health Center changed the outward appearance of The Queen's Medical Center as much as Ossipoff's tropical modernism had in 1960. The new look, with its columns, decorative ironwork railings, and soft colors seems to acknowledge the past while looking to the future. Existing structures were also revitalized to meet new challenges.

Built in 1960 to accommodate 10,000 patients a year, the overcrowded 'Iolani emergency room saw approximately 28,000 patients in 1998.[42] Queen's clearly needed a larger ER for a statewide population that had grown from 632,772 in 1960 to 1,211,537 in 2000.[43] A decision was made to gut the first two floors of the Pauahi Wing and build a new ER on the first level. Access would be via Miller Street, where a large ambulance bay would be constructed. The $14 million, 25,000 square foot ER opened in 1999. The ambulance bay was completed in 2000.

Although emergency cases had been accepted at The Queen's Hospital since its founding, emergency rooms as we know them today did not exist. Getting a patient to a hospital was a slow and tortuous process. Emergency patients arrived via horse-drawn ambulance over dirt roads. In 1911, building improvements made emergency care more accessible. Stairs at several locations had been replaced with inclines, so that "it was now possible, with the help of elevators, to convey patients in a 'wheeled truck' from the ambulance wagon at the front to any point in the Hospital without encountering any steps."[44]

That year, the annual report stated that "the Hospital holds itself ready to render free first aid in all cases of emergency and accident. The emergency operating room is placed immediately at the front entrance of the Hospital. Our professional staff is called on at all hours of the day and night."[45]

However, admitting infectious patients to the hospital posed a danger to other patients. In 1914, a controversy erupted over the refusal to admit an emergency patient determined to be infectious. As a result of the controversy, Queen's provided for an "emergency hospital" at which first aid would be given to all emergency cases, provided that certain conditions were met. This event appears to be the first step toward the establishment of an official emergency room. About 150 emergency patients a year were being treated at that time.

When the emergency room was housed in the Queen Emma Building (Nalani) in 1924, "the bid of the von Hamm Young, Co., to furnish a G.M.C. Ambulance painted maroon color with the name of the hospital painted thereon for $3,600.00 was accepted."[46] However, the Police Patrol often picked up the severely injured. Patients were first taken to the "emergency hospital" at the Police Station, then transferred to Queen's. In 1925, severely injured patients were brought directly to the hospital, "thus saving time and avoiding unnecessary suffering by the double transfer." An admitting doctor and a graduate nurse were in charge of emergencies.[47]

Emergency service was reinforced by the City and County Emergency Room built at Queen's in 1930 (Maluhia), while the hospital still operated its Queen Emma Building ER. The 1931 report of the medical director said of Maluhia that "it is a costly unit, if measured in dollars, but it has been most worth while in terms of reduced agony."[48] That year, there were 345 fracture cases, of which 109 were of the lower limbs, 70 of the upper limbs, and 47 of the skull, representing a large percentage of surgical admissions.[49]

By 1950, about 4,000 emergency cases were being treated yearly. That figure jumped to 6,922 in 1952. In 1970, when the number had grown to 24,000, a psychiatric social worker was added to the ER staff. As late as 1978, when Queen's formed a trauma team for major emergencies, the concept of a trauma

center was associated more closely with the battlefield than with civilian life. However, the Queen's ER became the first to be fully prepared for trauma patients twenty-four hours a day. The state Department of Health named the Queen's ER as Hawai'i's lead trauma center in 1981.[50] When the new ER was finished in 1999, it was hard to imagine that the 28,000 yearly emergency patients would match the greatly increased patient capacity. However, in 2008, the Queen's Emergency Room saw approximately 48,500 patients.

The Queen's Same Day Surgery Center (SDS) opened in 2000, replacing a smaller unit begun in 1982. The SDS was given a prominent location on the ground floor of Pauahi under the new ER, allowing patients access in front of the medical center. The SDS has been described as "a part of the wave of the future in health care," which delivers quality care with leading edge equipment and a "holistic, healing

City and County Emergency Unit on the corner of Punchbowl and Miller streets, 1930.

opposite

A Queen's trauma team hones their skills on a high tech, total body simulator. *Clockwise from left front:* Blake Smith, MD; Joe Iran, ER technician; Sharon Moran, MD; and Tiffany Aubert, RN.

environment."[51] Service is designed to move the patient effortlessly from registration to procedure and discharge through a discrete exit. The SDS features six operating rooms and four procedure rooms. Services include general surgery; ophthalmology; plastic and cosmetic surgery; dermatology; laser surgery; ear, nose, and throat procedures; orthopedics; gynecological services; and pain management. A large waiting area with wood finish floors and indirect lighting behind curvy, architectural elements along the ceiling represent a trend in hospital design. With comfortable furniture, area carpets, and artwork on the walls, the design has more in common with a resort than a medical institution. The look and feel of the Same Day Surgery Center set the tone for other projects.

The Emergency Room and SDS projects made necessary convenient parking accessible from the front of the medical center. The closest space available was the Miller Triangle, across the street from the main campus. The solution was to build an auto and pedestrian tunnel under Miller Street. When the 540-stall Miller Parking Garage was completed in 2001, cars were able to drop patients off at the front entrance

to Queen's and proceed to the parking garage via the tunnel. Parking for physicians, which had been located on the front lawn, was moved to the new garage. This allowed for a complete relandscaping of the front lawn, which was reverted to a garden design.

The 1960 lobby, which extended outward from Nalani, was remodeled in the 1990s, but then was completely replaced in 2004. The new lobby features echoes of the past—a café, wood finish floors, and high ceilings—and items that were cut from the 1924 building budget: marble countertops, and a porte cochere, were added in front of the SDS to improve traffic flow. In keeping with the new trend begun with the SDS, the design is more hotel than hospital, with its patio lanai, koa paneled reception desk, gift shop, and inlaid flooring.

In November 2004, the Queen's Women's Health Center opened at the back of the new lobby. A complete range of diagnostic, therapeutic, and preventive services for women became available, including mammograms, classes, and massages. The design, with its incandescent lighting, floral motifs, dark wood furniture, and wood finish flooring, eschews the look of a conventional hospital.

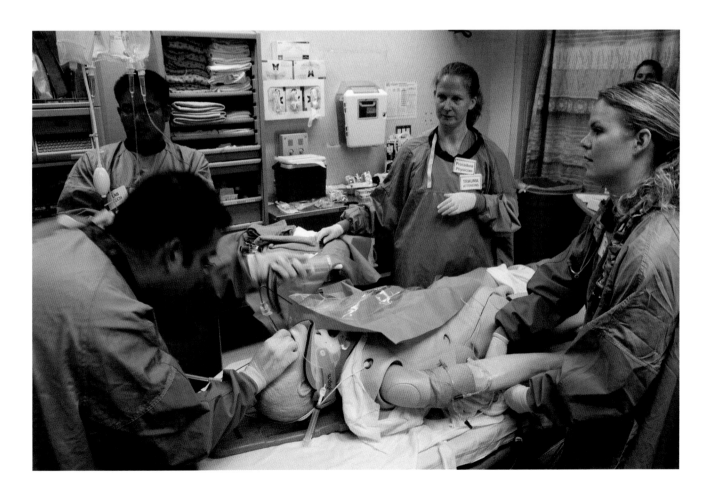

Queen's volunteer Steve Akana serenades visitors and staff in the Queen's lobby, continuing a long tradition of music performed in the buildings and on the grounds. The current lobby and entrance extends outward from the 1924 Nalani Wing, and includes items cut from that building's budget: marble counter tops and a porte cochere out front. Echoes from the past also include a café, wood finish floors, and a high ceiling.

opposite, from top
The Queen's Cancer Center reception area. Opened in 2007 in Kīna'u 1, the Queen's Cancer Center is a focal point for almost every aspect of cancer diagnosis and treatment.

The Queen's Women's Health Center is located at street-level in the Nalani Wing. The entrance is to the rear of today's lobby in the area where the 1924 lobby and entrance were located.

A New Concept in Hospital Design

The last two levels of the Queen Emma Tower were completed in 2003. The two levels, 5 and 6, were designated for the Neuroscience Institute and the Cardiac Comprehensive Care Unit, respectively. The process of designing the floors began in 1999, when Queen's was faced with the need to increase the number of beds for a growing number of acutely ill patients.

The two floors reflect new standards in hospital design. Rather than hallways, patient areas have an open design using glass to enhance the visibility of patients and the nursing units. Curvilinear ceiling architecture with changing colored lighting offers a change from the traditional hospital look, while matching patterns and colors on the flooring subtly direct visitors to their destinations. Local artwork, decorative borders, and valances create a less formal feel. Only work areas have direct lighting. Decentralized work areas have eliminated central nurses' stations, bringing caregivers closer to patients. Patient charts are available on wireless computers on wheels, and images such as X-rays and MRIs can be viewed on high-resolution monitors throughout the unit, eliminating the need for films.

Reminiscent of Dr. Hillebrand's recognition that the *kokua* contributed to a patient's well-being, the two floors allow the patient's family and friends to be a part of the healing process. Each room features a sleeper chair and Internet access for visitors, and a lounge allows family members to be close but separate, to rest and have meals.

Neuroscience at Queen's

The concept of a neuroscience unit at Queen's began when a beloved trustee suffered a stroke. In Hawai'i, stroke is the leading cause of disability and the third leading cause of death. The Queen's Neuroscience Institute (NSI) was established in 1996 to help the many people who suffer from neurological disease or injury. Since that time, the NSI has grown from a neuro-intensive care unit to a center of excellence that includes a full range of services, including a Stroke Center, Epilepsy Center, movement disorder clinic, and neurosurgery. The NSI's scope includes leading-edge research and outreach to the community.

Abreast of leading institutions in the United States and the first in Hawai'i, the Queen's Stroke Center is designed for comprehensive treatment that includes the elements of the stroke "chain of survival."[52] Much like a trauma team, an acute stroke team assembles to evaluate incoming stroke patients and takes appropriate action, which may include blood-clot-dissolving medications to restore blood flow to the brain quickly, minimizing damage. The NSI also launched a four-bed epilepsy monitoring unit in 2003 to map the brain waves of epilepsy patients during seizures and began participating in national and international research studies offering experimental treatments to patients, making Queen's the first hospital in Hawai'i to be a part of the FDA approval process.

Research: A New Standard of Discovery

Research has occurred at The Queen's Hospital since its earliest days. In 1863, Dr. William Hillebrand reported on his studies of leprosy:

The rapid spread of that new disease, called by the natives "Mai Pake"... is the genuine Oriental leprosy, as has become evident to me from the numerous cases which have presented themselves at the Hospital. Repeated investigations leave but little doubt ... about the contagious character of the disease, as I have followed its gradual spreading from a single person to many people in the same village.... I have devoted the wooden house which served as a temporary hospital [Kapa'akea's structure]... to the reception of this class of patients. In some of them medical treatment has produced a sensible amelioration.[53]

In the nineteenth century, doctors largely carried out their own investigations. The need for a pathologist at the hospital was recognized as early as 1907. As the first permanent pathologist in 1922, Dr. Nils P. Larsen's research progressed on a small scale as time permitted. In 1925, the first research grant was awarded to Queen's for the study of ultraviolet radiation.[54] Other early research focused on cancer, bacillus acidophilus (beneficial bacteria), fish poisoning, dental decay,

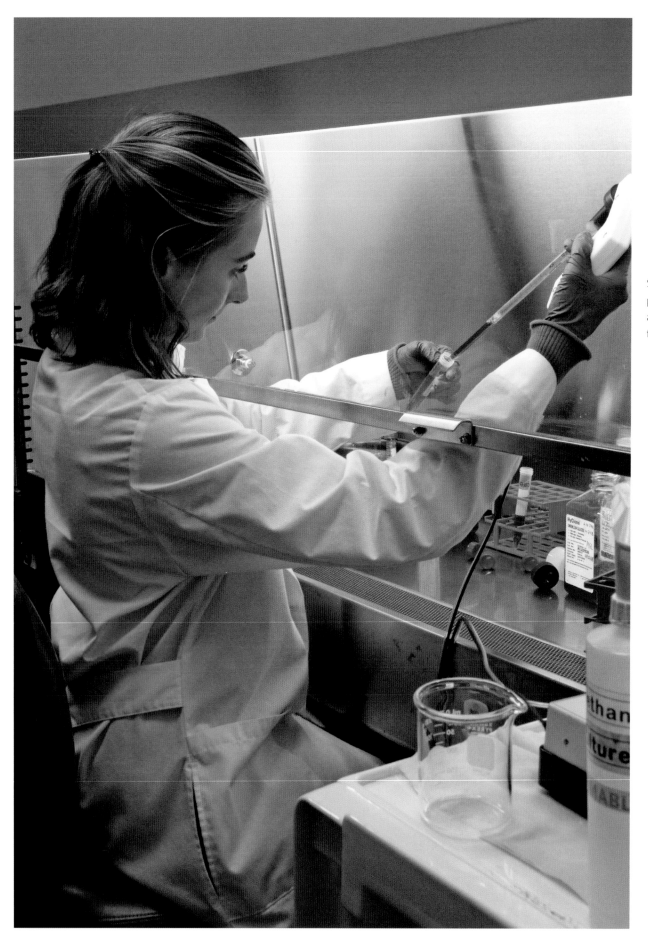

Suzanna Zierler, PhD, prepares cell cultures at the Queen's Center for Biomedical Research.

Markus Thiel, MD, PhD, (seated) and Maurice Needham, PhD, study how cells communicate via electrical charges at the Queen's Center for Biomedical Research. This "language" between cells is important in studying the origin and development of autoimmune diseases like diabetes.

and infant mortality on plantations. Research was suspended during World War II, but soon after, research grants were awarded.

Research was separated from pathology in 1960, and in 1963, laboratories were greatly expanded and given space with an addition on top of the 'Iolani Wing, primarily for research animals.[55] Notable research was conducted on cardiovascular disease in Hawai'i and on diabetes prevention. In the 1990s, research was formalized with the creation of a department to focus resources and expand services to Queen's physicians.

To be established as a world leader in health care, a medical center must perform both basic and clinical research. Toward the end of 1997, The Queen's Medical Center established the Center for the Study of Neurological Disease in collaboration with the University of Hawai'i. Located in the University Tower, the research facility is now called the Queen's Center for Biomedical Research (QCBR). Conducting research at the single-cell level, scientists have made discoveries that could lead to revolutionary treatments for diseases such as stroke, cancer, and diabetes. Discoveries with implications for immune system response and allergies have also been made. A collaborative study with researchers at Johns Hopkins University and Northwestern University recently discovered that a drug once used for leprosy holds promise as a therapy against autoimmune diseases like multiple sclerosis, type 1 diabetes, and psoriasis.

A NEW STANDARD OF CARE

Magnet: A New Standard of Care

At the beginning of the twenty-first century, increased demands and expectations were placed on health care providers. Outcomes of care, patient satisfaction, and other indicators were increasingly being measured and publicized, and government continued to demand higher standards. In 2006, The Queen's Medical Center decided to take patient care to a new level and seek Magnet Recognition from the American Nurses Credentialing Center (ANCC). Of some 5,500 hospitals in the United States, fewer than three hundred have achieved Magnet Recognition.

The highest institutional honor for hospital excellence given by the ANCC, Magnet Recognition was created after a 1983 study by the American Academy of Nurses revealed that certain hospitals had exceptional staff retention rates, job satisfaction, and patient satisfaction. Researchers analyzed the data to identify "14 Forces of Magnetism" that characterized these exceptional hospitals. Although Magnet Recognition is given by a nursing organization, it qualifies institutions across departments, not just the nursing units. The medical center was up to Magnet standards in many areas, but the process forced staff to take a hard look to uncover weaknesses. The draft of the Magnet application produced a stack of documents seventeen inches high, and included the answers to 168 statements, 953 exhibits, over nine hundred referenced sources, and more than three hundred quotes from staff and physicians. Slimmed to the maximum fifteen inches, the application was sent to the ANCC in 2008. After a three month review, the application was unconditionally accepted by the reviewers.[56]

Acceptance of the application was followed by a site visit by Magnet appraisers in January 2009. On April 13, 2009, The Queen's Medical Center was officially given Magnet Recognition,[57] a culmination of over two years of effort. Art Ushijima, president of The Queen's Medical Center noted, "The ANCC calls Magnet [Recognition] a 'seal of approval for quality,' because a Magnet hospital must have superior patient outcomes and patient satisfaction."[58] It was not so much the end of 150 years, but the beginning of the next 150.

Looking Back to Sustain a Vision

It is sobering to think of the misery and death disease brought—and continues to bring—not just to the people of Hawai'i but also to humankind. A glimmer of hope merges out of the pages of history: a young king and queen determined to build a place of healing for their people.

The walk from The Queen's Medical Center to the Honuakaha smallpox memorial is one of reflection. Upon returning and facing Queen's on Punchbowl Street, one can almost see the two-story hospital, a hundred feet wide on a barren plain, with "the remarkable hill called the Punchbowl" as a backdrop. A horse-drawn carriage pulls up to the front of the hospital, and a queen emerges with two Englishwomen. The young queen must have had a sense of satisfaction, for she was about to share the new hospital—a vision come to fruition—with her two guests. She would enter and be engaged in what she loved: comforting her people face to face, with simple cordiality and warmth. Although physically small to our eyes, the hospital was large in the hearts of the people.

The image fades to be replaced by the modern-day medical center, but somehow, the spirit of the queen remains. And tucked in here and there, old among new, are reminders of Queen's long history, and the echoes of voices from the past. It is fair to say that the king and queen could not have imagined what their hospital is today, but their vision was a singular one of caring for the sick, whomever they may be— a duty that new leaders were meant to carry forward to the next generation, and to the next, as long as sickness shall exist. Having served their time, they pass on the vision to others as the ill and the injured continue to enter the doors of The Queen's Medical Center—the hospital of the Chiefess.

QUEEN'S TODAY

The Queen's Medical Center, located in downtown Honolulu, Hawai'i, is a private, 501(c)(3) nonprofit corporation, acute care medical facility. It is the largest private hospital in Hawai'i, licensed to operate 505 acute-care beds and 28 subacute beds. Queen's has more than 3,700 employees and over 1,200 physicians on staff.

As the leading medical referral center in the Pacific Basin, The Queen's Medical Center offers a comprehensive range of primary and specialized care services. Queen's is accredited by The Joint Commission (TJC) and is affiliated with VHA, Inc., the national health care alliance. It is also approved to participate in residency training by the Accreditation Council for Graduate Medical Education.

Mission Statement

To fulfill the intent of Queen Emma and King Kamehameha IV to provide in perpetuity quality health care services to improve the well-being of Native Hawaiians and all the people of Hawai'i.

Queen's Philosophy of Care

We believe that all people will be given care with dignity and respect in an environment which is sensitive to each person's beliefs, values, and culture. Each team member, patient, and family is committed to a collaborative approach in providing an environment that will promote healing of mind, body, and spirit. Our philosophy is extended in a place of harmony as guided by our founders, Queen Emma and King Kamehameha IV.

The Queen's Health Systems

The Queen's Health Systems is a not-for-profit corporation established in 1985 to bring expanded health care capabilities to the people of Hawai'i and the Pacific Basin. It is Hawai'i's oldest and pre-eminent family of health care-related companies, ranking thirteenth in size among Hawai'i's corporations with net revenues of approximately $516 million.

The Queen's Health Systems Companies

- The Queen's Medical Center
  CareResource Hawai'i (A joint venture of The Queen's Medical Center and Kuakini Health System)
- Hamamatsu/Queen's PET Imaging Center
- Queen Emma Land Company
- Queen's Development Corporation
- Diagnostic Laboratory Services, Inc. (A joint venture of The Queen's Development Corporation and Kuakini Development Corp.)
- Moloka'i General Hospital

Trustees of The Queen's Medical Center

The following list of trustees, from Queen's founding in 1859 to January 1, 2010, is as complete and accurate as Queen's historical records allow.

Adams, E. P.	1879–1887
Adelmeyer, Ray	1949–1951
Aiona, Rev. Darrow L. K.	2002–2007
Alailima, Cecilia, MD	1993–1994
Aldrich, William A.	1859–1865
Alexander, Henry	1968–1985; 1988–89
Allen, Elisha H.	1867–1877
Allen, W. F.	1903–?
Anderson, Mrs. Robert A. Jr.	1964
Andrade, Naleen, MD	2000–present
Andrews, Lorrin	?–1867
Anthony, J. Garner	1942–1958
Aoki, Paul S.	1999–2009
Armstrong, Rev. Richard	1859–1860
Atherton, Joseph B.	1886–1903
Atherton, LeBurta	1967–1985
Aull, William E.	1961–1986
Austin, James W.	1859–1869

Baird, W. H.	1901–1909
Banfield, Nathan F.	1961–1967
Bartow, Cornelius S.	1869–1881
Bates, Asher B.	1859–1864
Bell, Douglas B. II, MD	1990
Bell, R. G.	1945–1952
Berg, Karl H.	1977–1993
Berk, Morton E., MD	1966–1969
Bishop, Charles Reed	1859–1895
Bishop, E. Faxon	1893–1934
Bissett, James	1859–1860;
Black, Constance	1976–1978; 1986–2006
Black, E. E.	1945–1975
Black, Evelyn J.	2007–present
Bolian, George C., MD	1984–1985
Bolte, Cristel	1893–1901
Breeden, John R.	1981–1992
Brewer, Charles	1860–1863
Brown, Francis 'I'i	1961–67
Brown, George 'I'i	1918–1945
Brown, Kenneth Francis	1965–1998
Brown, Willard	1907–1915
Budge, A. G.	(dates not available)
Campbell, A. J.	1899–1922
Carpenter, Clara	1952–1983
Carpenter, T. W.	1958–1961
Carson, M.B.	1947–1967
Carter, Charles L.	1889–1895
Carter, George R.	1899–1911
Cartwright, Alexander J.	1863–1890
Cartwright, Bruce	1890–1899
Cartwright, Bruce Jr.	1915–1938
Castle, S.N.	1859–1886
Catts, Ann B., MD	1984–1992
Cazimero, Momi	1989–2004
Chikasuye, C.	1967–1985
Ching, Han P.	1999–2005
Chong, Clayton D. K., MD	2002–2005
Chong, Norman T. S.	2002–present
Cleghorn, Archibald S.	1869–1910
Cockburn, J. L.	1922–?

Cooke, Charles M.	1893–1897
Cooke, Mrs. J. Platt	1952–1967
Cooke, Samuel A.	1989–1991
Cornuelle, Herbert C.	1969–1976
Cox, Gilbert E.	1982–1988
Cummins, John A.	1885–1897
Cunha, Emanuel S.	1905–1907
Davis, Robert G.	1859–1865
Davis, William G., MD	1987–1995
Damon, Rev. Samuel C.	1859–1885
Damon, Samuel M.	1885–1890
Daulton, Mrs. F. Roy	1972–1974; 1978–1980
Davies, Theophil C.	1901–1912
Dayton, David	1899–1907
Delaney, Matthew S.	2004–2006
Dickinson, Porter	1949–1952
Dobbins, Ralph	1980–1985
Dole, Sanford	1889–1893
Dominis, John O.	1877–1889
Dowsett, James I.	1867–1898
Ena, John	1895–1901
Epstein, Roger H.	1995–2000
Everett A.P.	1860–1863
Fukeda, Ernest H. Jr.	2008–present
Fukino, Chiyome L., MD	2002
Galt, Carter	1931–1976
Galt, John R.	1922–1940
Gamble, Lester H.	1967–1999
Gartley, Alonzo	1909–1915
Glade, J. C.	1873–1881
Gordon, Robert S.	1977–2004
Goshima, Cyril K., MD	1992; 1995–1997
Goto, Unoji, MD	1972–1974
Gray, Mrs. Leland	1967–1969
Green, William L.	1859–1887
Gregg, David L.	1859–1862
Griffith, Richard L.	1989–1999
Grobe, James L., MD	2005–2008
Guild, Douglas	1965–1981
Guild, John	1918–1922

Hackfeld, Henry	1859–1863
Hackfeld, J. F.	1895–1902
Halford, Peter, MD	2001–2004; 2009–present
Hall, Edwin O.	1859–1883
Halsted, Ann L.	1992–1993
Hancock, Barbara	1980–1981
Hannahs, Neil J.	2005–present
Hanson, Carl	1959
Harris, Charles C.	1861–1881
Hastert, Margery	1958–1985
Hastert, Mark H.	1995–2002
Hatch, Francis A.	1919–1921
Hebert, A. J.	1953–1968
Hemenway, Charles R.	1934–1945
Henderson, Charles J.	1958
Henriques, Edgar	1917–1918
Henshaw, Marshall B.	1958–1959
Heuck, T. C.	1859–71
Hilton, Zola	1982–1984; 1990; 1994
Hodges, Carpenter	1958
Hoffmann, E., MD	1871–1883
Holdsworth, Capt. Henry S.	1859–1863
Holland, Charles M. Jr.	1976–1990
Holt, Karen M.	1997–2002
Honeywell, Charles F.	1939–1945
Hong, Robert A., MD	1999–2000
Iaukea, C. P.	1885–1899
Irwin, W. G.	1885–1905
Isenberg, D.P.R.	1905–1907
Isenberg, H. Alex	1903–1907
Ivers, Richard	1915
Jaeger, James	1916–1917
Jamieson, F. W.	1927–1930
Johnson, Horace	1924–1929
Jordan, E. W.	1905–1909
Judd, A. F.	1865–1869
Judd, Charles, MD	1985–1986
Kapena, John M.	1877–1887
Kawakami, Keiji	1975–1980
Kea, William C.	1953–1993
Keller, A. R., MD	1934–1960

Ladd, J.	1859
Lau, William K. K., MD	1991
Leong, Mrs. Allan	1974–1976
Lewis, Mrs. Hal	1966
Loh, Kevin, MD	1993–1997
Love, W. A.	(dates not available)
Lowrey, F. J.	1898–1914
Li, Victor Hao, PhD	1989–1992
Lipman, Shirley	1983–1984
Lui–Kwan, Ivan M.	1993–1994
Luke, K. J.	1961–1999
Lum, K. Y., MD	1969–1972; 1984–1992
Lusk, Jan	1987–1988; 1991
Mackintosh, Rev. A.	1881–1909
MacNaughton, Malcolm	1959–1985
Manaut, Frank J.	1977–1992
Marumoto, Masajo	1961–1967
May, Henry	1877–1884
May, Thomas	1886–1897
McCandless, James S.	1907–1915
McInerny, William H.	1903–1910
Miller, Slator M.	1948–1950
Moehonua, W. L.	1871–1875
Mokuau, Noreen, DSW	2003–present
Montgomery, John	1859–1876
Morgan, James A.	1940–1945
Morgan, James F.	1907–1911
Morton, Ronald, MD	1997
Mott-Smith, E. A.	1907–1911
Mott-Smith, John	1867–1877
Nielsen, John F.	1975–1976
North, W. W.	1906–1911
Nurse, Kenneth R.	1961–1985
Obana, William G., MD	2005–present
Oda, Caroline Ward	2006–present
Oda, Francis T., MD	1992–2003
Ohtani, Robb K., MD	2010–present
Okamoto, Gary A., MD	1995–1997; 2000–2004
Oshiro, Robert C.	1976–1988; 1992–2003
Ozaki, Robert H.	1992–1994

Parke, William Cooper	1865–1889	Stewart, James H., MD	1978–1980; 1985–1986
Parker, Rev. Henry H.	1889–1893	Stoney, R. Moffitt	1871–1875
Parker, Samuel K.	1887–1895	Strode, Joseph, MD	1958–1962
Paty, John H.	1875–1897	Sumner, George	1959–1963
Peck, L. Tenney	1916	Sutter, J. I.	1961
Pflueger, J. C.	1869–1873		
Phillips, H.	1960	Tenney, Edward	1903–1925
Pierce, James F., MD	1989; 1993; 1995–1998	Teruya, Thomas H., MD	1989–1992
Pietsch, Charles J. III	1992–1999	Tom, Benjamin, MD	1974–1976
Pinkerton, F. J., MD	1945–1974		
Potter, George	1910–1919	Von Holt, Hermann	1859–1865
Pritchard, Fred A.	1986–1990	Von Holt, Marry Martens	1911–1915
		Walker, Henry A. Jr.	1995–1997
Reinhardt, Edward L.	2004–2005	Walker, J. S.	1881–1893
Rice, Daniel Paul	1905–1907	Ward, A.L.Y.	1948–1973
Rhodes, Godfrey	1869–1886	Watanabe, Jeffrey N.	1989–1999
Roberts, Burton W.	1977–1985	Waterhouse, Henry	1896–1907
Robertson, Alexander G. M.	1918–1922	Waterhouse, John T.	1859–1861
Robertson, George M.	1859–1867	Waterhouse, John T. Jr.	1879–1896
Robinson, Mark P.	1885–1911	Waterhouse, John	1907–1915
		Webster, William	1859–1864
Sage, William H., MD	1976–1984	White, Frances, PhD	1995–2005
Savidge, Samuel	1859–1865	Wichman, Henry F.	1901–1909
Schaefer, Frederick A.	1867–1907	Widemann, Herman A.	1867–1899
Schmidt, Heinrich W.	1893–1901	Wilcox, Allen C. Jr.	1959–1976
Schroffner, Werner G., MD	1994	Wilder, Gerrit P.	1905–1909
Serikawa, Garrett	2004–present	Wilder, Samuel G.	1883–1887
Severance, A.	1865–1867	Wing, Adrienne, MD	1997–2002
Sherman, George	1919–1923	Withington, Paul, MD	1933–1939
Shingle, Robert W.	1914–1915	Wo, Julia C.	2005–present
Shirasu, Myron E., MD	1980–1982; 1987–1988	Wood, Arthur B.	1901–1905
Smith, Alex	1966–1976	Wood, Clifford B., MD	1920–1932
Smith, Allan A.	1995–2004	Wright, Chatt G.	1986–1991
Smith, George W.	1895–1918	Wyllie, Robert C.	1863–1867
Snow, Benjamin F.	1859–1860		
Snyder, Mrs. William L.	1985–1986; 1989	Yeaman, Eric K.	2007–present
Spalding, Philip E.	1923–1933	Yee, Clifford H. N.	1976–1985
Spencer, Stephen	1863–1867	Young, Alexander A.	1922–1924
Staley, Thomas	1863–1867		
Stangenwald, Hugo, MD	1875–1879	Zen, Thelma (Mrs. Harry S. K.)	1969–1993
Stapenhurst, Florens	1860–1861		

NOTES

HALE MAʻI O KA WAHINE ALIʻI: 1–15
HOSPITAL OF THE CHIEFESS

1. Thomas G. Thrum, "Honolulu Sixty Years Ago," *Hawaiian Annual*, 1914, 86.

2. Ibid., 92.

3. Ibid., 87.

4. Ibid., 88.

5. William Cooper Parke, *Personal Reminiscences*, rewritten and arranged by his son, William C. Parke (Cambridge: Cambridge University Press, 1891), 56.

6. Ibid., 60.

7. Ibid., 66–67.

8. The Queen's Hospital, Honolulu, undated booklet, circa 1921, 3, Queen's Historical Room (hereafter QHR).

9. Resolution of the Members of The Queen's Medical Center, 1984, QHR.

10. Robert Colfax Lydecker, Roster Legislatures of Hawaii, 1841–1918; Constitutions of Monarchy and Republic, Speeches of Sovereigns and President. Compiled from the official records by Robert C. Lydecker, published by authority of the Board of Commissioners of Public Archives (Honolulu: The Hawaiian Gazette Co., Ltd., 1918), 59.

11. Robert C. Schmitt, "Hawaii's Hospitals, 1931–1956," *Hawaiʻi Medical Journal* 15, no. 4 (1956): 338.

12. Ibid.

13. An Act to Provide Hospitals for the Relief of Hawaiians in the City of Honolulu and Other Locations, *The Civil Code of the Hawaiian Islands*, 1859.

14. *The Polynesian*, April 30, 1859.

15. Thomas G. Thrum, "The Kamehameha IV–Neilson Tragedy," *Hawaiian Annual*, 1906, 91.

16. *Nupepa Kuokoa*, August 1, 1863.

17. Measuring Worth, at www.measuringworth.com, consumer price index calculator.

18. Ralph S. Kuykendall, *The Hawaiian Kingdom: 1874–1893* (Honolulu: University of Hawaiʻi Press, 1967), 86–87.

19. "Public Meeting," *The Polynesian*, May 28, 1859.

20. The Civil Code of the Hawaiian Islands, 1859, 434.

21. "Public Meeting," *The Polynesian*, May 28, 1859.

22. "Public Meeting," *The Polynesian*, May 28, 1859.

23. Ibid.

24. Charter of Queen's Hospital, June 20, 1859, 1. Further quotes are from this document.

25. Resolution 1 at a meeting of the Trustees of The Queen's Hospital, April 28, 1863, QHR.

26. Measuring Worth, at www.measuringworth.com.

27. Dr. Willis T. Pope, "Dr. William Hillebrand, M.D., 1821–1886," *Thrum's Hawaiian Almanac for 1919*, Honolulu, 1918, 59.

28. *Hawaiian Gazette*, May 1, 1867.

29. Thrum, "Honolulu Sixty Years Ago," 91–92.

30. *Pacific Commercial Advertiser*, August 4, 1859.

31. "His Majesty's Speech Proroguing the Legislature," *The Polynesian*, May 7, 1859.

32. Charter and By-Laws of The Queen's Hospital, Honolulu, 1859, 10–12.

33. George S. Kanahele, *Emma, Hawaiʻi's Remarkable Queen* (Honolulu: The Queen Emma Foundation, distributed by University of Hawaiʻi Press, 1999), 102.

34. Measuring Worth, at www.measuringworth.com.

35. Kanahele, *Emma, Hawaiʻi's Remarkable Queen*, 104.

36. *Pacific Commercial Advertiser*, August 4, 1859.

37. Charles S. Stewart, *Journal of a Residence in the Sandwich Islands during the Years 1823, 1824, and 1825* (Honolulu: University Press for the Friends of the Library of Hawaii, 1970), 177.

38. *The Polynesian*, February 4, 1860.

39. Ibid., June 23, 1860.

40. Richard A. Greer, "The Founding of The Queen's Hospital," *Hawaiian Journal of History* iii (1969): 123.

41. Hawaiian Historical Society, Seventy-Second Annual Report for the Year 1963, 11.

42. *The Polynesian*, May 26, 1860.

43. "The Cornerstone of the Hospital," *Ka Hae Hawaiʻi*, July 25, 1860, 70.

44. Ibid.

45. When the box was opened in 1922 at the demolition of the original building, it was found that part of the soldering had given way and water had seeped in; all had crumbled except the *Pacific Commercial Advertiser*, the Bible, the Book of Laws, and the ambrotypes of the king and queen ("Contents of Cornerstone at Old Queen's Hospital," *Honolulu Advertiser*, November 5, 1922). A drinking fountain, supplied with water from the hospital's artesian well, was constructed from the original cornerstone at the Punchbowl Street entrance and was dedicated in 1944. The fountain is no longer there, but a piece of the cornerstone is on display in the Queen's Historical Room.

46. "Laying of the Cornerstone of the Queen's Hospital," *The Polynesian*, July 21, 1860.

47. Ibid.

48. Ibid.

49. *The Polynesian*, June 11, 1859.

50. *Ka Hae Hawaiʻi*, June 15, 1859, 2.

51. *The Polynesian*, November 24, 1860.

52. Measuring Worth, www.measuringworth.com, GDP deflator calculator (compares cost of materials and labor).

53. Report to Lot Kamehameha, minister of the interior, from C. R. Bishop, December 20, 1860, QHR.

54. *The Queen's Hospital Bulletin* 12, nos. 1–6 (1936): 5–7.

1. *Hawaiian Gazette*, April 29, 1885.

2. George S. Kanahele, *Emma: Hawaiʻi's Remarkable Queen* (Honolulu: The Queen Emma Foundation, distributed by University of Hawaiʻi Press, 1999), 3.

3. *The Polynesian*, February 2, 1856.

4. Ralph S. Kuykendall, *The Hawaiian Kingdom, 1854–1874*, vol. 2 (Honolulu: University of Hawaiʻi Press, 1953), 83.

5. Ralph S. Kuykendall, *The Hawaiian Kingdom, 1778–1854*, vol. 1 (Honolulu: University of Hawaiʻi Press, 1938), 396.

6. Ibid., 388–96.

7. June 5, 1850 entry, *The Journal of Prince Alexander Liholiho*, ed. Joseph Alder (Honolulu: University of Hawaiʻi Press for the Hawaiian Historical Society), 1967.

8. Kuykendall, *The Hawaiian Kingdom, 1854–1874*, 2: 35.

9. Ibid., 34.

10. Ibid., 35–36.

11. Ibid., 78.

12. Gregg Diary, May 19, 1856; Liliʻuokalani, Hawaii's Story by Hawaii's Queen, Boston, 1898, 12.

13. Kuykendall, *The Hawaiian Kingdom, 1854–1874*, 2: 83–84.

14. Ibid., 85–86.

15. Letter to Henry Neilson from Liholiho, October 12, 1859, Hawaiʻi State Archives.

16. Kuykendall, *The Hawaiian Kingdom, 1854–1874*, 2: 86.

17. Alfons L. Korn, *The Victorian Visitors* (Honolulu: University of Hawaiʻi Press, 1958), 33.

18. Ibid., 89.

19. Kuykendall, *The Hawaiian Kingdom, 1854–1874*, 2: 34.

20. *Pacific Commercial Advertiser*, August 28, 1862.

21. Ibid.

22. Ibid., 124.

23. Kenneth F. Brown, *In the Footsteps of Our Founders, Nā Meheu O Nā Aliʻi*, The Queen's Health Systems, 1996, 44–45.

24. Manley Hopkins, *Hawaii: The Past, Present, and Future of Its Island-Kingdom* (New York: D. Appleton and Co., 1869), 162, 466.

25. Ralph S. Kuykendall, *The Hawaiian Kingdom, 1874–1893*, vol. 3 (Honolulu: University of Hawai'i Press, 1967), 9–10.

MANAMANA: AT THE FOOT OF PUNCHBOWL   23–27

1. Gorman D. Gilman, "Streets of Honolulu in the Early Forties," Honolulu, *Hawaiian Almanac and Annual for 1904*, 1903.

2. Ibid., 24–25.

3. Cultural Surveys of Hawai'i, *Monitoring Plan in Support of The Queen's Medical Center Redevelopment Project*, Honolulu (Kona) District, Honolulu Ahupua'a, Island of O'ahu, October 2005, 23. Subsequent information about lots, streets, and property is from this source.

4. Queen's Hospital Memorandum, re Unfinished Business, February 1, 1912.

5. Cultural Surveys Hawai'i, 20.

6. Ibid.

7. The Queen's Hospital Annual Report, 1945, 20.

8. *Queen's Vision*, fall 1989, QHR.

9. Report to the Trustees of The Queen's Hospital, December 22, 1871, QHR.

10. "Queen's Parking a Perennial Problem," *Queen's Print Connection* 8, no. 33 (1998), QHR. Parking issues in the *Queen's Print Connection* were complied by Margery Hastert, Queen's historian.

11. Meeting of the Hospital Staff, Queen's Hospital, December 14, 1909, QHR.

12. "Queen's Parking a Perennial Problem," *Queen's Print Connection* 8, no. 33 (1998), QHR.

13. Letter to W. Roel, superintendent, from the secretary of the board of trustees, September 14, 1916.

14. *Queen's Messenger* (January 1964), QHR.

15. Report to the Social Services Department, The Queen's Hospital Annual Report, 1923, 29, QHR.

16. "Under a Spreading Banyan, Ricardo Lives On," *Queen's Print Connection* 16, no. 20 (2006): 3, QHR.

1. Alfons L. Korn, *The Victorian Visitors* (Honolulu: University of Hawai'i Press, 1958), 109–10.

2. *Pacific Commercial Advertiser*, December 6, 1860.

3. Ibid.

4. Ibid.

5. Clarice B. Taylor, "Tales about Hawaii," *Honolulu Star-Bulletin*, ongoing series, December 1955 to January 1956.

6. Korn, *The Victorian Visitors*, 110.

7. Report to the Board of Trustees of the Queen's Hospital by John Brodie, February 19, 1887.

8. Report of the Visiting Committee of The Queen's Hospital for the quarter ending December 31, 1907.

9. His Majesty's speech at the opening of the Legislature, April 7, 1855, 59–60.

10. Report of the Board of Health to the Legislative Assembly of 1882, 73.

11. Report of the Board of Health to the Legislative Assembly of 1884, xxxviii, lv, lvi, lxiii.

12. *The Polynesian*, June 29, 1861.

13. Laws of His Majesty Kamehameha IV: King of the Hawaiian Islands, Passed By the Nobles and Representatives, at Their Session, 1860, 33–34.

14. Ibid.

15. Richard A. Greer, "The Founding of The Queen's Hospital," *Hawaiian Journal of History* iii (1969): 127.

16. *The Polynesian*, December 29, 1860.

17. Ibid., October 1, 1861.

18. Trustee's Report, September 22 to December 21, 1873, QHR.

19. *The Polynesian*, July 6, 1861.

20. *Hawaiian Gazette*, July 14, 1869.

21. *Pacific Commercial Advertiser*, June 20, 1873.

22. Ibid., April 1, 1873.

23. Ibid., December 20, 1872.

24. Ibid., December 4, 1874.

25. Treasurer's Report by Chas R. Bishop, May 31, 1875, QHR.

26. Report of the Secretary of the Queen's Hospital, July 3, 1877, QHR.

27. Biennial Report, 1877–79, QHR.

28. John H. Paty, secretary pro tem, Secretary's Report, *Pacific Commercial Advertiser*, July 7, 1881.

29. Ibid.

30. Ibid.

31. *Pacific Commercial Advertiser*, December 22, 1871.

32. "Visit to Queen's Hospital," Hawaii Territorial Medical Society, 1904, 11.

33. Rule XII, House Rules of the Queen's Hospital, 1894, QHR.

34. Letters from the People, *Honolulu Advertiser*, August 11, 1935.

35. Ibid.

36. Ibid.

37. Lela M. Goodell, "Plantation Medicine in Hawaiʻi, 1840 to 1964: A Patient's Perspective," *Hawaiʻi Medical Journal* 54, no. 11 (1995): 786.

38. *Hawaiian Gazette*, April 29, 1885.

39. The Will of Emma Kaleleonalani, October 21, 1884.

40. "Alex Smith, Business Manger, Writes on the Queen Emma Lands," *Queen's Messenger* (July 1959), QHR.

41. "Queen Emma Trust Abolished," *Honolulu Advertiser*, March 8, 1967.

42. Proposed Amendments to the By-Laws of the Queen's Hospital, 1896, QHR.

43. Report of the General Superintendent of the Census, 1896, Department of Public Instruction, Republic of Hawaii, 28.

44. Ibid., 51.

45. C. B. Wood, MD, "The Queen's Hospital—A Reminiscence," The Queen's Hospital Bulletin, 1935, 11, QHR.

1. Letter to George W. Smith, Esq., secretary, Queen's Hospital, from Johannes F. Eckardt, superintendent, June 6, 1903, QHR.

2. "Pauahi Wing of Hospital Is Dedicated," *Pacific Commercial Advertiser*, June 24, 1905.

3. Measuring Worth, at www.measuringworth.com, GDP deflator calculator.

4. Contractor's Bond between John Ouderkirk, Principal, George Rodick, and J. F. Humburg, Sureties, and the Trustees for The Queen's Hospital, March 16, 1904, QHR.

5. William Cooper Parke, *Personal Reminiscences*, rewritten and arranged by his son, William C. Parke (Cambridge: Cambridge University Press, 1891), 78.

6. "Pauahi Wing of Hospital Is Dedicated."

7. Ibid.

8. Report to the Trustees by T. Clive Davies, president, December 31, 1911, QHR.

9. Letter to doctors promoting new Pauahi Wing, January 1906, QHR.

10. *Pacific Commercial Advertiser*, June 24, 1905.

11. Quarterly Report to the Trustees ending May 31, 1879 by Robert McKibbin Jr., Surgeon to the Queen's Hospital, QHR.

12. Report of the meeting of the Hospital Staff, November 10, 1909, QHR.

13. Robert C. Schmitt, "Medical Progress in a Remote Archipelago," *Hawaiʻi Medical Journal* 54, no. 11 (1995): 771.

14. Report of the Medical Director, Sixty-Fifth Annual Report of The Queen's Hospital, December 31, 1924, 18, QHR.

15. Joseph E. Strode, "The Progress of Medicine in Hawaii," Presidential Address, Transactions of the Hawaii Territorial Association, 1926, 17.

16. Letter from E. F. Bishop to L. E. Pinkham, president of the Board of Health, dated October 25, 1907, QHR.

17. Letter from Johannes Eckardt, superintendent, to George W. Smith, Esq., secretary, The Queen's Hospital, May 17, 1905, 1.

18. Ibid., 2.

19. Letter to L. E. Pinkham, president of the Board of Health, from George Smith, Esq., secretary, Queen's Hospital, November 14, 1905.

20. Trustee's minutes, 1907, QHR.

21. Charles R. Bishop as Treasurer in Account with the Queen's Hospital, Honolulu, Showing Receipts and Expenditures during the Half Year Ending December 20, 1873, QHR.

22. One Hundredth Semi-Annual Report of the Treasurer of The Queen's Hospital, Honolulu, T. H., ending July 15, 1909.

23. Letter to the Trustees from Johannes F. Eckardt, superintendent, June 6, 1903, QHR.

24. Letter to the Trustees from Robertson and Wilder, Attorneys-at-Law, August 17, 1903, QHR.

25. Trustees' document, circa 1909, QHR.

26. The Queen's Hospital Charter, 1909.

27. Figures provided by The Queen's Medical Center.

28. Schmitt, "Medical Progress in a Remote Archipelago," 771.

29. Case Book, no. 2, January 1, 1904 to May 31, 1905, The Queen's Hospital, 9-6-04, QHR.

30. Minutes of the Trustees, August 8, 1908, QHR.

31. The Queen's Hospital Annual Report, 1910, 5.

32. Letter to the president of the Board of Health, May 28, 1908, QHR.

33. Meeting of the Hospital Staff, October 7, 1908, signed by Johannes Eckardt, QHR.

34. Report, 1908, QHR.

35. Report, Surgical Operations, Queen's Hospital, December 31, 1910, QHR.

36. Robert C. Schmitt and Eleanor C. Nordyke, "Influenza Deaths in Hawaii," *Hawaiian Journal of History* 33 (1999): 103.

37. *Honolulu Star-Bulletin*, December 31, 1919, 4.

38. Report to the Board of Trustees of The Queen's Hospital by C. H. Allen, superintendent, November 19, 1919, QHR.

39. Schmitt and Nordyke, "Influenza Deaths in Hawaii," 101.

40. Joseph E. Strode, MD, FACS, "The Progress of Medicine in Hawaii," Transactions of the Hawaii Territorial Medical Association, 1926, 15.

41. Author's interview with Alice Yoshida, January 1, 2009.

42. "We Salute You Dr. Marie and Dr. Bob," *Queen's Vision*, June 1973, QHR.

43. Memoirs of Dr. Marie Faus, by Marie Faus, unpublished and undated, QHR.

44. Report to the Board of Trustees of The Queen's Hospital by C. H. Allen, superintendent, November 19, 1919, QHR.

45. Letter to T. F. Lansing, acting superintendent, Queen's Hospital, from Bruce Cartwright, secretary, Board of Trustees, October 16, 1925, QHR.

46. Author's interview with Ethel Matsui, RN.

47. President's Report of The Queen's Hospital Corporation, Honolulu, Sixty-Fourth Annual Report of the Queen's Hospital, December 31, 1923, 5, QHR.

48. Lela Goodell, "Plantation Medicine in Hawaii 1840 to 1964: A Patient's Perspective," *Hawai'i Medical Journal* 54, no. 11 (1995): 786–87.

49. Rodman Miller, MD, "Plantation Doctor," *Hawai'i Medical Journal* 54, no. 11 (1995): 791.

50. Goodell, "Plantation Medicine in Hawaii 1840 to 1964: A Patient's Perspective," 788.

51. Ibid.

52. Blake Clark, "Plantation Babies Okay Now," *Reader's Digest* 50, no. 297, January 1947, 127–30.

53. Marvin A. Brennecke, "Dr. Nils Paul Larsen," *Plantation Health* 29, no. 2 (1964).

54. Goodell, "Plantation Medicine in Hawaii 1840 to 1964: A Patient's Perspective," 788.

55. Measuring Worth, www.measuringworth.com, GDP deflator calculator.

56. President's Annual Report of The Queen's Hospital Corporation, Sixty-Fifth Annual Report of The Queen's Hospital, December 31, 1924, 4, QHR.

57. Letter to Charles Ingvorsen, September 13, 1922, QHR.

58. Letter from Bruce Cartwright, secretary to the Board of Trustees, dated September 13, 1922, QHR.

59. "The Architecture of C. W. Dickey," State Historic Preservation Division, at www.hawaii.gov/dlnr/hpd/hpcal184.htm.

60. "From 'Horse and Buggy' to High Technology," *Honolulu Star-Bulletin*, July 27, 1984, A-10.

61. *Queen's Messenger* (March 1943), QHR.

62. Author's interview with Leatrice Nakashima, RN, April 6, 2009.

63. Letters to George C. Potter, superintendent, from Bruce Cartwright, secretary, Board of Trustees, 1923–26, QHR.

64. Mrs. Herbert M. Dowsett, "The Development of the Occupational Therapy Department of The Queen's Hospital, Honolulu, Hawaii," *Occupational Therapy and Rehabilitation* 13, no. 2 (1934).

65. *The Sales Builder*, October 1936, 9.

66. Dowsett, "The Development of the Occupational Therapy Department of The Queen's Hospital, Honolulu, Hawaii."

67. Margery Hastert, Queen's Historian, "Looking Back at Orthopedics," undated article, QHR.

68. "Nurses Move into New $250,000 Quarters," *Honolulu Star-Bulletin*, May 17, 1932.

69. Report of the Medical Director, Seventy-Sixth Annual Report of The Queen's Hospital, December 31, 1935, 15, QHR.

70. William J. T. Cody, MD, "Psychiatry in Hawaii, A Short History," *Hawai'i Medical Journal* 33, no. 6 (1974): 208.

71. Author's interview with Jean Grippin, RN, March 16, 2009.

72. *Hawai'i Medical Journal* 16, no. 5 (1957): 560.

73. Minutes, Meeting of Doctors at Interne's cottage to discuss plans for new additions to Queen's Hospital, September 24, 1941, QHR.

74. "Queen's Plans 100-Bed Wing," *Honolulu Advertiser*, August 1, 1941.

75. Ibid.

76. *Billings Gazette*, Billings, MT, December 8, 1963, 10.

77. "'Navy Wife' Rests after Pearl Harbor," *Abilene Reporter*, Abilene, TX, September 3, 1942, 6.

78. Ralph B. Cloward, MD, "War Injuries to the Head," *Journal of the American Medical Association* 118, no. 4 (1942): 267–70.

79. "'Navy Wife' Rests after Pearl Harbor," 6.

80. "What Would You Do in an Air Raid?" *Montana Standard*, Butte, MT, February 8, 1942.

81. *The Capital*, Annapolis, MD, December 7, 1991.

82. *Billings Gazette*, December 8, 1963, 10.

83. "Principles of Traumatic Surgery," *Hawai'i Medical Journal* 1, no. 3 (1941): 141–42.

84. Elizabeth D. Bolles, "War Came to Hawaii," *Hawai'i Medical Journal* 50, no. 9 (1991): 313–14.

85. *Queen's Messenger* (September 1943), QHR.

86. "Who Wears What?" *Queen's Messenger* 11, no. 2 (February 1943): 3, QHR.

87. Measuring Worth, www.measuringworth.com, GDP deflator calculator.

88. Annual Report, The Queen's Hospital, 1945, 21.

89. Ibid.

90. "Palama Settlement has Connection to Queen's," *Queen's Print Connection* 6, no. 25 (1996).

91. Jeanne Ambrose, "Looking Back on History of Queen's Hospital Here," *Honolulu Star-Bulletin*, July 27, 1984, A-10.

THE TRAINING SCHOOL FOR NURSES 109–121

1. Frances R. Hegglund Lewis, *History of Nursing in Hawaii* (Node, WY: Germann-Kilmer Co., 1969), 55.

2. Minority Report from Charles L. Carter to the Queen's Board of Trustees, January 6, 1893, QHR.

3. Letter from Johannes F. Eckardt to Miss Ida Shannon, January 6, 1912, QHR.

4. Report to the Board of Trustees by Geo. C. Potter, superintendent, May 25, 1926, QHR.

5. "From 'Horse and Buggy' to High Technology," *Honolulu Star-Bulletin*, July 27, 1984, A-10.

6. Author's interview with Ethel Matsui, RN, April 2009.

7. Author's interview with Elaine Kawamoto, RN, April 2009.

8. Ibid.

9. "In Second Vote Nurses Choose Union," *Honolulu Star-Bulletin*, August 23, 1974.

10. "Nurse Turnover Rate Declines at Queen's," *Honolulu Star-Bulletin*, February 17, 1981.

11. Ibid.

12. Report to the Trustees, December 31, 1911, QHR.

13. The story of Nina Cook was told by her daughter, Miran Ovenden Herman, who corresponded with the Queen's historian Margery Hastert in the 1960s.

14. The Annual Report of The Queen's Hospital, 1916, 21–22.

15. Author's interview with Nancy Kim, RN, April 2009.

16. *Queen's Messenger* 11, no. 2 (February 1943): 4, QHR.

17. The Queen's Hospital, undated booklet, circa 1921, 8, QHR.

18. "Report of the Superintendent of Nurses," The Queen's Hospital Annual Report, 1916, 21.

19. Report to the President and Board of Trustees by J. T. Warren, Chairman of the Visiting Committee, October 29, 1918, QHR.

20. Author's interview with James Stewart, MD, April 20, 2009.

A NEW STANDARD OF CARE 1950–PRESENT   123–160

1. Newspaper clipping, 1956, QHR.

2. "Hawaii's Remarkable Health Record," *Honolulu Star-Bulletin*, December 27, 1958.

3. Newspaper clipping, 1956, QHR.

4. "Symbol of a King and Queen," *Paradise of the Pacific*, June 1953.

5. "Colorful Pageant Marks New Wing Dedication," *Queen's Messenger* 13, no. 8 (November 1954): 1, QHR.

6. Measuring Worth, www.measuringworth.com, GDP deflator calculator.

7. "Colorful Pageant Marks New Wing Dedication," 2.

8. *Queen's Messenger* 14, no. 2 (February 1955): 1, QHR.

9. "Dedication Tomorrow of Queen's New Surgical Wing," *Honolulu Star-Bulletin*, October 12, 1954.

10. Ibid.

11. *Ka Hoku Loa*, July 1864, 26.

12. The Transactions of the Medical Society of the State of California, Thirty-First Annual Session, Sacramento, vol. 31, April 1901, 228.

13. Ibid., 235–36.

14. "Queen's Opens Advanced Technology ORs," *Queen's Print Connection* 14, no. 38 (September 13, 2004): 1, QHR.

15. "QMC Builds Premier Surgery Program," ibid., 14, no. 9 (February 23, 2004): 1.

16. "Queen's Brings Robotic Surgery to Hawaii," ibid., 16, no. 8 (February 19, 2007): 2.

17. Ibid., 2.

18. "1959 Sees Much New Construction and a Surgical 'First' at Queen's," *Queen's Messenger* 22, no. 1 (January 1960): 2, QHR.

19. "Queen's Heart Celebrates Reopening," *Queen's Print Connection* 17, no. 34 (August 18, 2008): 1, QHR.

20. Scott C. Brainard, "How Open Heart Surgery Came to Hawai'i," *Hawai'i Medical Journal* 54 (November 1995): 794.

21. Ibid., 795.

22. Ibid., 794.

23. "Remote Technology to Speed Heart Attack Treatment," *Queen's Print Connection* 17, no. 25 (June 16, 2008): 1, QHR.

24. Measuring Worth, www.measuringworth.com, GDP deflator calculator.

25. "Hospital Enters Push-Button Age," *Sunday Advertiser*, July 24, 1960, F-2.

26. *Queen's Print Connection* 7, no. 44 (October 27, 1997): 1.

27. Ibid., 16, no. 45 (November 5, 2007): 1.

28. Measuring Worth, www.measuringworth.com, GDP deflator calculator.

29. "Queen's New Wing to Open," *Sunday Star-Bulletin and Advertiser*, May 23, 1971.

30. "Accent on Privacy at Queen's Medical Center," *Honolulu Star-Bulletin*, May 13, 1971.

31. "Hospital Has a Waiting List," *Honolulu Advertiser*, July 10, 1971, A-14.

32. Administrator's Report, Annual Report, 1967–68, 21, QHR.

33. "110 Years Old and Growing," *Honolulu Advertiser*, July 23, 1970.

34. "Queen's Dream Comes True," *Sunday Star-Bulletin and Advertiser*, September 29, 1968.

35. Tomi Knaefler, "Queen's Starts $3 Million Mental Health Facility," *Honolulu Star-Bulletin*, July 1, 1971.

36. "Helistop Gives Quick Access," *Sunday Star-Bulletin and Advertiser*, Honolulu, May 1, 1977, J-10.

37. "POB III Opens in Grand Style," *Queen's Print Connection* 16, no. 34 (August 14, 2006): 1, QHR.

38. Author's interview with Setsuko Yoshida, RN.

39. Measuring Worth, www.measuringworth.com, GDP deflator calculator.

40. Jeanne Ambrose, "Queen's Medical Center Facing New Challenges," *Honolulu Star-Bulletin*, July 27, 1984, A-10.

41. "Dept. of Native Hawaiian Health Established," *Queen's Print Connection* 12, no. 30 (July 22, 2002): 1, QHR.

42. "QMC Has Designs on New ER," ibid., 8, no. 28 (July 6, 1998): 1.

43. U.S. Census Bureau.

44. Report to the Trustees by T. Clive Davies, President, December 31, 1911, QHR.

45. Ibid.

46. Letter to George C. Potter, superintendent, from Bruce Cartwright, secretary, Board of Trustees, January 23, 1924, QHR.

47. National Hospital Day, May 12, 1925, booklet published by The Queen's Hospital, QHR.

48. Report of the Medical Director, The Queen's Hospital Seventy-Second Annual Report, 1931, QHR.

49. Ibid.

50. Report, 1981, QHR.

51. *Queen's Print Connection* 10, no. 16 (April 17, 2000): 1, QHR.

52. Ibid., 14, no. 32 (August 2, 2004): 1.

53. "Report of Dr. W. Hillebrand, Surgeon to the Queen's Hospital, April, 1863," Supplement to the Report of the President of the Board of Health, 1886, Leprosy in Hawaii, Extracts from Reports of the Presidents of the Board of Health, Government Physicians and Others, and from Official Records, Report of the President of the Board of Health to the Legislative Assembly of 1886, on Leprosy.

54. Queen's History, 1925–30, unpublished document, QHR.

55. "Addition to Queen's Being Built," *Honolulu Advertiser*, December 19, 1962.

56. *Queen's Print Connection* 18, no. 17 (April 20, 2009): 2, QHR.

57. Arthur Ushijima, "Magnet Recognition Truly an Honor," ibid., 3.

58. Ibid.

ACKNOWLEDGMENTS

Many people have helped make this book possible. Their assistance, encouragement, and stories have added a richness that would otherwise be lacking.

A heartfelt mahalo goes to the following individuals who have freely shared their stories: Elaine Kawamoto, RN; Nancy Kim, RN; Ethel Matsui, RN; Leatrice Nakashima, RN; James Stewart, MD; Alice Yoshida; and Sets Yoshida, RN. A special thanks goes to Jean Grippin, RN, who has a wonderful memory for stories from the past, served as a reader of the manuscript, and has offered a lot of encouragement during the process of writing this book.

Sincere thanks go to the following people who contributed to the research for this book. Much of the material they found or the leads they provided were invaluable to the telling of the story of Queen's: Ann Catts, MD, Carolyn Ching; David Forbes; Keith Harada; Sue Kachiroubas; and David Kikau Jr. A special mahalo goes to Maria B. J. Chun, PhD, who not only helped collect a sizable quantity of material but also did exceptional work in organizing some very confusing information. She also took a keen eye to much of the manuscript.

Many thanks also go to the individuals who facilitated the writing of this book. They read, commented, advised, found resources and volunteers, used connections, and/or went out of their way to free up time to allow this book to be written: Chris Bailey; Roy Cameron; Ellyn Fukuda; Ruth Honda, RN; Jeannine Johnson; Kathleen Kimura; Maggie Magee, RN; the Rev. Al Miles; Marlene Oishi; Beverly Parker; Diane Paloma; Barbara Pope; and Sharlene Tsuda. Much gratitude goes to Glee Stormont for taking care of details that otherwise would have considerably bogged down the process of research and writing.

A warm mahalo goes to Richard Mamiya, MD, who established the Mamiya Medical Heritage Center, which has helped to preserve the rich history of The Queen's Medical Center, and to the late Margery Hastert, Queen's beloved historian to whom this book is dedicated. Special thanks goes to President Arthur Ushijima, QHS/QMC, for his foresight in making this history of Queen's available to the people of Hawai'i.

Thanks also go to many others who offered encouragement, support, and help along the way. To all, it is humbly hoped that this book will in some small way enrich your knowledge of not only The Queen's Medical Center but also of Hawai'i, the place we call home.

ILLUSTRATION CREDITS

Illustrations in this book are mainly from the collections of The Queen's Medical Center. The following illustrations from various other public and private collections are reproduced with permission and are listed below.

Page i. [Detail] *Royal Palm Trees on Queen's Hospital Grounds.* n.d. Photograph by Taber of San Francisco, Calif. Bishop Museum, Honolulu.

Page xiv. *Queen Street, Honolulu.* 1856. Watercolor over graphite on paper by George Henry Burgess. Honolulu Academy of Arts; gift of Mr. and Mrs. Don Severson in honor of the Academy's seventy-fifth anniversary, 2002 (27,084).

Page xvi. *Woman of Honolulu.* 1852. Watercolor over pencil on paper by Carl Johan Alfred Skogman. The National Library of Sweden, Manuscripts, Ms. S. 76.

Page 2. *No. 6. View of Honolulu from the Catholic Church.* 1853. Hand-colored lithograph by Paul Emmert. Collection of Sam Cooke, Honolulu.

Page 3. *Upper Fort Street, Honolulu (Nuuanu Valley).* 1857. Watercolor over pencil on paper by George Henry Burgess. Honolulu Academy of Arts; gift of Judge and Mrs. Walter F. Frear, 1941 (11,635).

Page 3. *View of the Smallpox Hospital, Waikiki.* Circa 1853. Oil on canvas by Paul Emmert. Hawaiian Historical Society, Honolulu.

Page 4. [Detail] *No. 6. View of Honolulu from the Catholic Church.* 1853. Hand-colored lithograph by Paul Emmert. Collection of Sam Cooke, Honolulu.

Page 7. [Detail] *No. 6. View of Honolulu from the Catholic Church.* 1853. Hand-colored lithograph by Paul Emmert. Collection of Sam Cooke, Honolulu.

Page 9. *Man of the Hawaiian Islands.* 1852. Watercolor over pencil on paper by Carl Johan Alfred Skogman. The National Library of Sweden, Manuscripts, Ms. S. 76.

Page 12–13. *View of Honolulu from Punchbowl Crater.* Circa 1865. Photograph by Charles Leander Weed. Bishop Museum, Honolulu.

Page 16. *Alexander Liholiho (Kamehameha IV) and Emma Nāʻea Rooke.* Circa 1856. Gold, double-framed daguerreotype. Reproduction photograph of the daguerreotype by Linny Morris. Collection of Daughters of Hawaiʻi, Honolulu.

Page 18. *Emma Nāʻea Rooke and John Kalaipaihaihala Young II (Keoni Ana).* Circa 1850. Daguerreotype. Bishop Museum, Honolulu.

Page 18. *Prince Lot (Kamehameha V), Dr. Gerritt P. Judd, Alexander Liholiho (Kamehameha IV).* 1850. Daguerreotype. Bishop Museum, Honolulu.

Page 24. *Bombax or shaving brush.* 1998. Watercolor on paper by Geraldine King Tam. Collection of Geraldine King Tam, Kapaʻa, Kauaʻi.

Page 25. *The Queen's Hospital.* Circa 1870s. Stereo view by Menzies Dickson. Collection of Dean and Marsha Curry, Benicia, Calif.

Page 30. *The Queen's Hospital.* 1880s. Photographer unknown. Hawaiʻi State Archives, Honolulu.

Page 37. *Exterior View of The Queen's Hospital.* 1890. Photographer unknown. Bishop Museum, Honolulu.

Page 38–39. *View of Honolulu from Punchbowl.* 1894. Photographer unknown. Bishop Museum, Honolulu.

Page 46. *The Queen's Hospital.* n.d. Photographer unknown. Hawaiʻi State Archives, Honolulu.

Page 56. *The Queen's Hospital Ambulance.* 1910–1915. Photograph by Ray Jerome Baker. Bishop Museum, Honolulu.

Page 69. *Pau Hana.* 1929. Oil on canvas by Shirley Russell. Collection of Dean and Marsha Curry, Benicia, Calif.

Page 90. *Harkness Hall (Nursing Students' Residence).* 1935. Photograph by Pan-Pacific Press Bureau. Hawaiʻi State Archives, Honolulu.

Page 91. *The Queen's Hospital.* n.d. Photograph by Pan-Pacific Press Bureau. Hawaiʻi State Archives, Honolulu.

Page 108. *Exterior View of The Queen's Hospital.* 1940. Photographer unknown. Bishop Museum, Honolulu.

Published by
THE QUEEN'S MEDICAL CENTER
1301 Punchbowl Street
Honolulu, Hawai'i 96813
www.queens.org

ISBN 978-0-615368-82-5
LCCN 2010927401

Illustrations are from The Queen's Medical Center
collection unless noted otherwise on page 175.

Reproduction photography of The Queen's Medical Center
collection of photographs and documents by Hal Lum and
Masayo Suzuki. Medical artifacts in The Queen's Medical
Center collection photographed by Hal Lum and Masayo
Suzuki. Contemporary photographs of The Queen's Medi-
cal Center by Hal Lum and Masayo Suzuki (pages iv, xii–
xiii, 61, 73, 88–89, 92–93, 134–135, 154–155, 157, 158, 159); and
Jason Kimura (pages 27, 153).

Designed and produced by Barbara Pope Book Design.
Printed in China.